CHILDREN OF
THE HANDCRAFTS

CHILDREN OF
THE HANDCRAFTS

by Carolyn Sherwin Bailey

WITH LITHOGRAPHS BY GRACE PAULL

THE VIKING PRESS · NEW YORK

First published October 1935

Second printing December 1935

Third printing December 1941

Fourth printing April 1944

Fifth printing February 1946

Sixth printing May 1952

Seventh printing January 1957

Eighth printing May 1964

COPYRIGHT 1935 BY CAROLYN SHERWIN BAILEY
RENEWED 1962 BY REBECCA DAVIES RYAN
PUBLISHED BY THE VIKING PRESS
PRINTED IN THE UNITED STATES OF AMERICA
DISTRIBUTED IN CANADA BY
THE MACMILLAN COMPANY OF CANADA, LTD.

Contents

THE SAMPLER 11

    Telling the story of Lora Standish, who made
the first American sampler.

WHITTLING JOHNNY 23

    Told from records of old Rhode Island in the
days of the Puritans. The story has for its back-
ground the jackknife trades that developed many
inventions still in use.

THE CLOCK-MAKER'S APPRENTICE 33

    The story of Macock Ward, a boy apprentice to
the clock-making trade in old Connecticut. He
left us many beautiful examples of timepieces:
clocks from homes, steeples, and belfries.

THE SILVERSMITH'S ADVENTURE 44

    The boy Paul Revere, and his later influence upon
the silver craft of our country.

THE GARDEN MERCY PLANTED 55

    About the first garden in Bath, New Hampshire,
planted and tended by Mercy Harriman, nine-
year-old daughter of an early settler.

THE BOY WHO LOVED TOOLS 65

    Duncan Phyfe and his times.

CHRISTMAS SHIP   75
   The carving of figureheads in old Salem.

BETSY'S NEW HAT   86
   This story, found in old Providence, Rhode
   Island, records the making of the first straw hat
   in the Colonies by a twelve-year-old girl, Betsy
   Metcalf, who started our hat industry.

WHEN JOSHUA MADE A BOOK   95
   A boy's composition book, home-made, recorded
   the building of the first school in Buffalo. Saved
   from the Buffalo fire in 1813, it is preserved as a
   precious bit of handwork, together with its story.

COVERED-WAGON BOY   105
   About Daniel Moyer, a boy of Conestoga days,
   who grew up to drive the wagons he had helped
   make, and who met General Lafayette.

STAR-SPANGLED BANNER GIRL   115
   About Caroline Pickersgill of old Baltimore, a
   girl who helped make the flag about which our
   national anthem was written.

THE BOY WHO MADE PENCILS   126
   The boyhood of Henry Thoreau, helper in his
   father's pencil factory.

LOST IN THE APPLE CAVE   136
   An unpublished story of Johnny Appleseed
   from the record of a covered-wagon child who
   met him unexpectedly.

A BASKET FOR THANKSGIVING   146
   About Nathan Hunt, a famous basket-maker of
   New England, and some children who knew him.

QUILT OF MANY STARS   156

American quilts were the tapestry of our history,
taking their designs from the lives of settlers and
pioneers. The story is based on the diary of a
quilt-maker of Ohio.

SYLVANUS'S NEW BREECHES   167

About the old trade of hand-tailoring, and a
boy who ran away to escape the designs of the
traveling tailoress of Coventry-Benton, in New
Hampshire.

THE FOURTH OF JULY SURPRISE   181

Early printing, and the story of Simeon Ide, vet-
eran newspaperman of Vermont. The story in-
cludes the celebration of the Fourth in a Vermont
village, sixty years ago.

BOOK TRAILS   187

Full Page Illustrations

THOMAS BONEY, THE DUXBURY SHOEMAKER   15

THE PEDDLER IN THE KITCHEN   22

IN DUNCAN PHYFE'S SHOP   71

FIGUREHEADS IN THE SHIPYARD   79

"SISTER" SHIPS   85

BETSY METCALF'S STRAW BONNET   93

JOSHUA'S LOG-CABIN HOME IN BUFFALO   99

THE BLACKSMITH   109

THE FLAG AT THE FORT   123

HENRY THOREAU'S CABIN   134

JOHNNY APPLESEED, ROSE, AND THE BEAR   141

THOMAS THE HERB MAN   151

THE QUILTING BEE   163

THE SUGAR CAMP   171

IN THE PRINTING SHOP   183

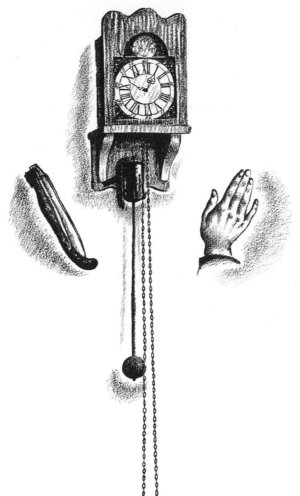

A BOOK of true stories of boys and girls of our early history who had a share in the development of the handcrafts which helped build our civilization. The stories have been built from genealogical records, personal letters and diaries, rare village and county records, and a study of old maps that give them a flavor of their periods and an appeal for our present emphasis upon the arts and crafts.

THE SAMPLER

LORA STANDISH left the village street behind and climbed up, up through sweet-smelling fields and orchards until she reached the top of Captain's Hill. There she could see across the bay to Plymouth, where she had lived when she was a little girl, too young to remember it well. Below Captain's Hill lay the town of Duxbury, and nestling at the foot of the hill, like a flawless white pearl in a setting of emeralds, was the Standish farm, The Nook. Captain Standish, Lora's father, had bought the fertile acres of The Nook, built the stone house with its low thatched roof, and moved the family over from Plymouth about the year 1632. Lora loved every tree, flower, and sound of their home. Looking down and over the countryside, Lora followed the boundaries of the

11

village as she and her brothers, Alexander, Myles, and Josias, had trailed them, gathering berries and nuts. They had looked over Captain Standish's shoulder as, with quill pen and home-made ink, he outlined the map of Duxbury.

"The Bounds between Duxbury and Plymouth: From a little brook running from Stephen Tracy's to another little brook, falling into Black Water from the Commons, left, to Duxbury and thereabouts," Lora repeated to herself, tracing the map in the clear blue air with one toil-hardened hand. But boundaries made dull thinking compared with the vision down in the valley.

She saw forests of pine, maple, birch, and cedar in which to wander. Sometimes Lora and the other children would catch a glimpse of an Indian in his cloak of deer or wildcat skin, a terrifying picture against the darkness of the trees. Sometimes a faint bird-call or a whistle like that of a tree-toad would warn them that red men were near. But the Standish boys and Lora were not really afraid of Indians. Captain Standish, the brave leader of Plymouth from the coming of the Pilgrims, had made friends with these fierce forest-dwellers. Lora could just remember the great chief, Massasoit. One of the treasures which they had moved from Plymouth—along with the settle, the feather beds, the warming pan, the pewter, the jugs, and the andirons—was the green embroidered cushion upon which Massasoit had sat, as on a throne, when he first visited Captain Standish and made peace with the Pilgrims.

Next to the woods of The Nook, Lora loved Pine Brook, singing over its stones and gurgling with joy when a little girl, supposedly washing flax, shed her hobnailed shoes and knitted stockings, and waded into the clear water. She loved the smell of corn-grinding at the mill, where Indians and settlers brought their grain to be made into flour and meal. Pilgrims in worn garments of homespun and red men with headdresses of feathers and fox-tails greeted one another as they emptied their corn into the mill's hopper. Beaver Pond beside the mill had a "roof" of sweetly growing pond lilies, white and pink. In the dugout boat that Alexander had made, the children floated among the lilies and Lora played that she was the lady of an old English castle, the Standish castle, about which Barbara, her mother, had told her such stirring tales.

Turning to the blue bay, Lora looked toward the sea, and dreamed of England. Her mother had come to be Captain Standish's helpmate after the death of beautiful Rose, his first wife. Barbara had been brave indeed to exchange her comfortable English living for the hardships of Plymouth. Only occasionally did Barbara Standish tell Lora of that other Duxbury, the ancestral hall of the Standish family in England. Looking across the waters that separated the two Englands, Lora Standish remembered her mother's homesick words.

"A great stone castle with a moat. The halls hung with portraits of warriors in helmets and corselets, of lawyers with peaked beards and stiffly starched ruffs, and of courtiers with slashed dresses and flowing lovelocks. Your father, Lora, was a Standish of Standish. He was a soldier under Queen Elizabeth before he took the long journey on the *Mayflower* to this new land."

Lora touched distastefully her gray kersey petticoat, her stout jacket of homespun linsey-woolsey, and her blue fustian apron. She undid her long yellow braids and released the gold shower of her hair to be tossed by the breezes. She was pretending that she was the daughter of a lord, and that the Saturday work, from which she had run away, did not exist.

The wind rippling the waves of Lora's fair hair brought sounds in its wake. The ringing of a blacksmith's hammer down in the village. The whir of spinning wheels set in open doorways. The soft lowing of cattle. The clack-clack of wooden looms. The sound of beating bundles of flax stalks into fine strands. Saturday in old Duxbury was not a day of leisure. Lora knew that she was needed at home. Hastily replaiting her hair, she ran down the hill toward The Nook.

Again, though, she let her impulse guide her. Instead of turning into the road that led between fields of corn and apple orchards to the white Standish farmhouse, Lora followed the village street as far as the shop of Thomas Boney, the Duxbury shoemaker. The village shoemaker knew everything that went on in town, for all the shoes, great and small, found their way to his threshold sooner or later. Sitting at his bench, tap-tap-tapping away at wooden pegs or hobnails, Thomas Boney listened and then gave out the news. So many little pigs born at Elder Brewster's estate. A girl to be publicly reprimanded because she had worn full lace sleeves to church meeting. A second notice from the village magistrate that children tending sheep or cattle in the fields must spin, knit, or weave as they walked. There was a group of boys at the shoemaker's door, and Lora joined them.

Her brother Alexander was there. He pointed to a sign hung on Thomas Boney's door:

"Herrings to be caught on Saturdays and Mondays between sunrise and sunset."

Thomas Boney was giving out another piece of news: "A wildcat has been seen prowling about at the edge of the village," he said. "The town treasury will pay twenty shillings for that cat's pelt, to man or boy. And the crows are making havoc in the cornfields. Sixpence will be paid from the town treasury for a dead crow."

Alexander gripped Lora's arm. "Come on home and help me get my fowling-piece and bullets," he urged. "We will get Myles, Josias, and the fish-nets. You, Lora, shall fetch and carry for us, and we will spend the whole day shooting crows, catching herrings, and hunting the cat."

That did sound like fun! Because she had no sister and had grown up with boys, Lora Standish was as good a hunter, as lucky a fisherman, as her brothers. All thought of the work waiting for her at home left her mind. Flying down the street from the shoemaker's shop, Alexander and Lora sped toward home. In Lora's fancy, those shillings and pence from the town treasury were all spent for ribbons, quilted silk bonnets with flowers, and long lace sleeves suitable for a little lady of Standish Hall.

As they hurried home, Alexander and Lora passed their friends: young shepherds, herdsmen, and farmers working in the fields. Small looms, upon which garters, suspenders, and belts were woven, could be carried as a little girl followed her lambs or geese. Good spinners had small wheels with them there in the meadows, twirling their spindles as

they walked. Patience, Thankful, and Prudence, busy and painstaking young Pilgrims, hardly glanced at Alexander and Lora.

Myles was in the cornfield, but at his brother's shouted news about the bonus for killing a wildcat, Myles dropped his hoe. Josias could always be lured away from the grindstone to go fishing. Lora went into the house to fill a rush basket with lunch. Her mother, Barbara Standish, stood before the loom weaving a blue-and-white bedspread.

"Ah, Lora," she exclaimed. "Where have you been so long? I need some skeining done. Come hither, little daughter, and help me."

Lora stood dutifully in front of her mother holding the yarn as Barbara skeined it. She helped to wind the white warp on spools and set the spools in place. From the time when she was five years old, Lora had done her share of the spinning. As soon as she could stand on a footstool and reach the wheel, she had begun making thread and yarn.

When the loom was again set in motion, Lora took Alexander's fowling-piece from its place in the corner and set it outside the door, ready for the boys. She went back and touched her father's sword, a shining blade that hung above the row of muskets. It looked out of place in this homely New England home, for it was a Damascus blade, slender, polished, and carved.

Captain Standish had brought this sword of his ancestors from England in the *Mayflower,* as a reminder of past glory in this untracked wilderness. His sword had been carried by the Crusaders in their battles for their faith. The Pilgrims, wanderers from home in the same cause, looked upon Captain Standish as a Crusader. Holding Lora in his lap, and pointing to the play of light upon the slender blade from the blazing pine-knots on the hearth, Captain Standish had told his little daughter stories of the great ladies who watched from castle towers as the knights rode away.

Looking up for a moment from her weaving, Barbara Standish also caught the sword's silver gleam.

"This would be a good day to finish stitching your sampler, Lora. When I was a girl in England at your age, I could work the fern, the Queen's, the feather, Spanish, rosemary, and mouse embroidery stitches. The ladies of my mother's time stitched patterns upon the silk banners that the knights carried to war. If you are industrious, my Lora, perhaps you can finish your sampler today."

Lora sighed, but there was no questioning her mother's command. From the garden came a boy's shrill whistle, the signal that if she was going with them for the day's sport, she must make haste. They would be off without thinking of lunch. They would gather berries, cook fish over a wood fire, and roast ears of corn. Lora rubbed her eyes to keep back the tears a Standish never allowed to fall. Opening her sewing bag, seating herself in a straight-backed chair, she began setting tiny stitches in the oblong piece of coarse homespun linen that was her sampler.

"How does one show that a lamb has two legs on each side of his body?" she asked her mother.

"Stitch them in thread of a different color," Barbara told her.

Lora bent her fair head over her sewing, trying not to hear the calling of the blackbirds in the corn, the wind whispering through the open door, "Come out and play, little girl." With great care, and counting each stitch, Lora lettered this verse upon her sampler:

> Lora Standish is my name.
> Lord, guide my heart that
> I may do Thy will:
> Also fill my hands with
> Such convenient skill
> As may conduce to virtue
> Void of shame;
> And I will give the glory
> To Thy name.

The Pilgrim samplers were needlework picture-books with trees, animals, flowers, birds, and people all stitched in colored thread, which was spun and dyed by the children themselves. Every little girl had finished her sampler before she was twelve.

*   *   *

A field of flax planted in front of a thatched cottage as soon as the stones were cleared away. Sun and rain to open the blue flowers and ripen the stalks. Washed in the brook, dried in the sun, combed, tied in bunches, watered, washed again, beaten, separated, spun, woven—that was the way the flax was made into cloth for the sampler. The children helped, dipping the flax fibers in the brook to wash them, laying them in the sun to bleach, sitting patiently beside the flax wheel to spin the long, even threads, washing the skeins again in the brook.

At last they covered the sampler with stitched pictures and ABC's, the verses they copied from the Bible, or such a wish as Lora sewed into hers, that her hands might be filled with "convenient skill." In exquisite cross-stitching, Lora had put the alphabet upon this piece of linen, and now she was working on the verse. Lora's sampler was going to be very fine indeed.

*   *   *

The little town of Duxbury, across the bay from Plymouth, still basks in the sunshine. Crows talk of the weather and stuff themselves with corn, safe from the fowling-pieces of the Standish boys. Orchards and gardens, where once stood the home of Myles Standish, dream of a little girl who gave up a long-ago Saturday's fun to finish her sampler. It was the first piece of beautiful embroidery left to us from the skillful hands of a Pilgrim child. With her father's sword, an old iron pot, and a pewter dish, Lora Standish's sampler may be seen in the Pilgrim Hall of Plymouth, telling us how, three hundred years ago, handcraft began in our country.

WHITTLING JOHNNY

THE FLAMES from the kitchen fireplace shining on the peddler's two battered tin trunks in the corner turned them into silver. Snuggled on the settle at one side of the fireplace, with the old peddler, Chepa Rose, beside him, Johnny Helme thought that the trunks might be the treasure chests of a pirate, and Chepa Rose himself the pirate. Years of tramping lonely roads and climbing the bleak hills of Rhode Island, with those two tin trunks hung over his back by a harness of stout hempen webbing, had weathered Chepa Rose to the color of an Indian. Every farmhouse in the Narragansett country, and as far as Connecticut, knew the old peddler. He was as much a part of the seasons as the plowing and the harvesting.

23

He had been invited to spend the night at the Helme farm because Johnny's mother needed to have the family umbrella mended as only Chepa Rose could mend it. And he had brought with him a preparation of sulphur for whitening home-made straw bonnets. Johnny's sister was waiting to have her new bonnet bleached when the umbrella was again waterproof. Johnny wished there were even a chance of his sharing the contents of the peddler's trunks. Besides Chepa Rose's jugs of ink that he made himself, his wooden spoons and tinware, ribbons and almanacs, they carried spinning tops and colored-clay marbles, hard candy, and Barlow knives.

How Johnny Helme's fingers ached to clasp a Barlow knife! His old case knife was worn so thin from sharpening that he expected the blade to break any day, and it was not a Barlow knife anyway. Barlow knives were made of finely tempered steel. They were big enough to make popguns, a bow and arrows, or a rabbit trap. They would last all a boy's young days, but they cost too much for Johnny to buy. He had no money anyway.

As Chepa Rose finished fitting a new rib in the umbrella, he took his own jackknife out of his pocket and cut his initials in tiny letters in the handle. He snapped the knife shut and put it back in his pocket, looking shrewdly at Johnny. "You want a new knife?" he asked. "Chepa Rose brought Barlow knives, but only one is left." He went over to his trunks and took out a new almanac, opening the pages in the flickering firelight to one on which a poem was printed. "Pastor John Pierpont wrote this about boys' jackknives," he said. "Read it."

Johnny's mother lighted another candle, and the boy read
the poem aloud. Everyone listened: Johnny's father slumped
in a rush-seat chair, tired from his day in the fields; Johnny's
mother and big sister, patient figures in blue homespun,
scouring the wooden trenchers and tankards in which supper
had been served. Johnny could read aloud very well.

The Yankee boy, before he's sent to school,
Well knows the mysteries of that magic tool,
The pocket knife. To that his wistful eye
Turns, while yet he hears his mother's lullaby.
And in the education of the lad,
No little part that implement hath had.
His pocket knife to the young whittler brings
A growing knowledge of material things;
Projectiles, music, and the sculptor's art,
His chestnut whistle and his shingle dart,
His wooden popgun with its hickory rod,
Its sharp explosion, and rebounding wad,
His corncob fiddle and the deeper tone
That murmurs from his pumpkin-leaf trombone
Conspire to teach the boy. To these succeed
His bow, his arrows of a feathered reed,
His windmill, raised the passing breeze to win,
His water-wheel that turns upon a pin.
Thus by his genius and his jackknife driven
Ere long he'll solve you any problem given;
Make you a locomotive or a clock,
Cut a canal or make a floating dock;
Make anything, in short, for land or shore,
From a child's rattle to a seventy-four.
Make it, said I—yes, when he undertakes it,
He'll make the thing, and make the thing that makes it.

Johnny brought his reading to a choked stop. His heart was so filled with the glory of owning a Barlow jackknife, and the impossibility of buying one, that a great tear splashed down on the almanac and his voice shook. Chepa Rose looked searchingly into the boy's face.

"You want a new knife?" he asked. "You want Chepa Rose's last Barlow knife? Wait! In the morning, before I start on the road again, I will show you how to get that knife."

Johnny, dreaming of whittling arrows and carving a water-wheel, tossed and wriggled about all night on his hard corn-husk mattress. He hurried through his breakfast porridge and joined Chepa Rose, who had been up and out before sunrise. He found the peddler in the woodshed, busily whittling on a yellow-birch sapling about five inches thick, which he had cut down in the woods and brought back before breakfast. He put the little tree into the boy's hands and instructed him how to go on with the work.

"Make the stick as tall as Chepa Rose," he said, "six feet. About a foot and two inches from the big end cut a ring around the bark. Cut off all the bark below this ring. Then cut slivers, thin and flat, up to the bark ring, leaving their top ends attached to the stick. Cut out the little core that is left. Take off the bark above the ring and begin cutting slivers down. Leave a stick just thick enough for a handle. Tie the slivers above the ring down tight over the others with a piece of that tow string your father uses for his grain-bags. Then trim their ends off even. Whittle the handle smooth and make a hole in the top for a loop of cowhide. Look, boy!"

Following Chepa Rose's directions carefully with his old

knife, Johnny saw something grow in his hands. He had made a fine birch broom, very much needed in those long-ago days. Chepa Rose chuckled. "Sell it," he advised Johnny. "Make more. Sell them, and when Chepa Rose comes by this way next time, buy his Barlow knife." The peddler went into the house, strapped his trunks over his back and was soon only a humped shadow, fading at last into the winding road.

It was a wooden age in that part of our land, Rhode Island, which had been settled by the Puritans. Driftwood was washed up by the sea; veined and mottled knots of maple wood were carved by the Narragansett Indians into smooth, close-grained bowls for the housewives; odd crooked and deformed boughs were gathered by the children in the woods to make sled runners, yokes for pigs and geese, and pot racks for the kitchen. Young birch trees were prized for fashioning their only brooms.

Every child and grown-up needed to know how to whittle. Scythes, rakes, hoes, ax-handles, hay hooks, cheese-hoops, butter paddles, and the great wooden blocks of wood hollowed out to hold porridge or stew, and called "trenchers,"

were made at home from wood. Even the youngest children
could shave off elm and brown ash to make the splints used
for chair seats and doormats. Wild red-cherry wood was
gathered, sawed, split, and whittled into shape for ax-handles.
Maple wood was split and whittled into shoe pegs that had to
be made by the bagful for the village shoemaker. And
brooms! The day Chepa Rose started on the road again,
Johnny Helme began his broom making. He knew that the
town storekeeper of Kingston, the nearest village to the
Helmes, paid but sixpence apiece for yellow-birch brooms,
but that was better than nothing. If only Chepa Rose held
to his word, Johnny thought, about keeping that last Barlow
jackknife until he could pay for it!

Johnny liked his work. He tramped alone through the
forest looking for young birch trees, getting hungry from a
day out in the air, meeting an occasional Indian looking for
laurel to carve into spoons. He spent good long days out in
the woodshed, slivering the brush for his brooms and polishing the whittled handles with a piece of broken glass until
they glistened. When he had finished a dozen he tied them together and slung them over his back. The Kingston store was
more than five miles from their farm and his way lay over
Tower Hill, where an old meeting-house raised its white roof
above the sea like a sentinel. It was a lonely way into Kingston
Village. Old tales told of witches riding through the air above
the meeting-house chimney. Johnny had to help with the
farm chores, so it was mid-afternoon before he started out
with his brooms; and the days were getting short, with an
early twilight.

Johnny began his five-mile trip bravely. The sand road over the flat lands near their farm offered easy going, and the salt tang of the sea was in his nostrils. But a dozen hardwood brooms made no light pack for a boy ten years old, even for a country boy well used to roads and hills. And soon he left the plain behind to climb the wooded hill on the other side of which lay the village. In the forest there were strange noises. The thud of a dropping nut, the chatter of a squirrel, the shrill call of a jay, Johnny knew, might be the sign of an unfriendly Indian. He had a real scare when what he took to be a redbird suddenly loomed before him as a tall Indian with a scarlet feather in his braided hair. But the Indian gave the boy a friendly nod as he saw his load of brooms. He, too, was a broom-maker.

At the top of the climb Johnny came to the meeting-house washed white as a lighthouse by the rain and snows. On Sunday, the meeting-house was alive. Horses with Indian saddles were fastened outside, and ladies and gentlemen in the bright costumes they had brought from England—far too rich for church Johnny's mother thought—gathered about the door. Once, the church records said, the light from many torches flaming outside the meeting-house had told the country-side that a witch had been caught and was shut up there until she could be taken away for her trial. Johnny hurried a little. What was that? The darkness had settled down around him and far above the chimney of the meeting-house he could hear the flutter of wings.

Chepa Rose had told of the days it was thought that ill-ness, bad weather, disaster of whatever kind was the work of a witch living in the neighborhood in the form of some old woman. At night the witches took their true shapes and rode through the sky upon broomsticks, working evil as they went. Johnny was suddenly paralyzed. He could not move. There he was with enough brooms on his back to supply steeds for twelve witches. He could feel their long fingers snatching him, pack and all, up to the top of the meeting-house and dropping him when they had taken the brooms.

But he remembered the new jackknife for which he was working and tried to stop the rapid beating of his heart. A soft wing brushed his cheek. Why, there were no witches; only the homing swallows flying in and out of the meeting-house chimney before settling down for the night. Johnny shifted his brooms upon his aching back and ran along until he reached the dark village street and the store. He was too tired to do more than stack the brooms against the counter and try to get his breath again.

The storekeeper pointed to the cracker-barrel, cut a thick slice from a yellow cheese on the counter, and told Johnny to help himself. He was glad to buy the well-made brooms. He sometimes stocked a hundred brooms at a time, for they did not last long in those days of bare floors and daily sweeping. He paid Johnny and kindly offered to lend him a lantern for the dark five-mile walk home. Johnny would see that the lantern was returned by some ox-cart or horseback rider in a day or two. The jingle of the silver in the pocket of his patched homespun breeches was a heartening tune all the long way home. A few weeks more of broommaking, two more trips to Kingston Village, and the peddler's Barlow knife would be Johnny Helme's.

Everybody was in bed, the moon was high, and there was frost on the fields before the boy reached home that night. He whistled as he came along. Not a boy in school would have a better jackknife than he. All those dream toys of which he had read in Chepa Rose's almanac, popguns, a corncob fiddle, a toy windmill, were going to be his, the work of his hands like the brooms that would earn the knife.

Chepa Rose, the Narragansett peddler, tells in an old letter this story of Johnny Helme, the young broom-maker. We may be sure that the Barlow knife found its way into Johnny's hands, and perhaps it is among the old jackknives preserved from our Colonial handcraft days, in the Smithsonian Institution at Washington, or in Deerfield Memorial Hall at Old Deerfield, Massachusetts. Daniel Webster owned a Barlow jackknife and was proud of it. But there could have been no greater happiness of ownership than that of Johnny Helme.

That Rhode Island country of the jackknife trade still lies tranquil and green along the sea. The wooded hills, the soft-voiced streams and blue lakes, the ancient hill-path made first by the Narragansett Indians over which Johnny Helme carried his brooms to market, may be visited by boys and girls of today. But a witch riding her broomstick over Tower Hill would be picked off by an airplane in no time, and the old farms are covered by the beautiful homes of present-day Newport and Narragansett summer residents. Machines turn out by thousands the wooden implements that had to be made by hand in the old days of our country, but if we think of it, there is scarcely an article of everyday use that was not shaped first by a knife. And although Johnny Helme's many times great-grandsons ride over the hills today in automobiles, there is not one of them who would not be proud to own and whittle with Johnny's jackknife.

THE CLOCK-MAKER'S APPRENTICE

MACOCK WARD, clock-maker's apprentice, stood on the threshold of his master's shop and peered longingly in. He was twelve years old, his brief school days were over, and he was bound out to the skilled clock-maker, Ebenezer Parmele, for his clothes, board, and bed until he should be twenty-one years old. Ebenezer was the only clock-maker in Guilford, Connecticut, at that time, about the year 1714. The entire village looked up to him, for within his clattering, tool-strewn shop there was being put together the first public clock of the State of Connecticut. It was to be placed in the tower of the village meeting-house when it was finished. No wonder Macock had been pleased to come to work for the clock-maker. Ebenezer was a man of wide experience. He could build boats. In a boat he had made with his own hands when he was little more than a youth, he had sailed to New York. There he had learned the craft of clock-making in the shop of old Bogardus, the Dutch silversmith. Returning to

Guilford, Ebenezer had made rush-seat chairs until he had earned enough money to buy his lathe, hammers, forge, turning wheel, and the other tools needed for clock-making. Now he had the best shop in Connecticut, for he understood working in wood and so could make the frames for his clocks as well as the works. Sometimes, in those days, the villagers had to hang their clocks without frames, called "wag-on-the-walls," from a hook where, unprotected by frames from dust and knocks, they soon got out of order. But Ebenezer Parmele could make both brass and wooden clocks.

Macock, a barefoot, homespun-clad youngster, watched with envy the other apprentice boy, Ebenezer's nephew Abel Parmele, who was busy in the shop hammering a great brass clock dial. Although Abel was a year younger than Macock, his uncle Ebenezer was allowing him to work at the trade, while Macock must serve first as servant, kindling the forge fire in the mornings, running errands, and blowing the shop bellows. How Macock wished that he might be in Abel's place, beating the soft brass, so fresh and pliable from the mold, into a burnished clock face! Abel was working with intensity, bent over the anvil. The circle of brass, held in a vise, lay on the anvil where Abel tapped, tapped, smoothing, spreading it out, and bringing it gently to the thinness which his uncle would later polish, engrave, decorate with a delicate design of flowers or a great amusing moon face, and place in front of the wheels in a new clock.

There were brass wheels to be molded, hammered, and assembled. The hands, pillars, and pendulums must also be shaped with delicate skill. With the click of the small hammer on the metal, the ticking of grandfather clocks, half

finished as they stood in the corners, the clatter of banjo and lantern clocks, hung in various stages of construction on the wall, this old shop was a merry, exciting place. Macock knew that he was disobeying his master's orders as he stepped across the threshold of the shop. The corn-patch needed hoeing. There was wood to chop for Mistress Parmele's baking oven. But clock-making was Macock's dream. Abel was too busy to notice him. Softly Macock moved about the shop, touching the tools, scenting the fragrance of wood, dazzled by the sunlight on polished brass and silver.

This old shop was like nothing else in New England in those days. The clock-maker had to be a cabinet-maker, a designer, a foundryman, an engraver, a blacksmith, and a pattern-maker. It was said that Ebenezer Parmele had made his smaller tools, painstakingly shaping files, hammers, and saws, in the days when he was building his ship for the trip to New York. A bag of tools carried on a man's back meant his fortune in those days.

Besides the scrap metal waiting to be melted in the crucible, tempered in the forge fire, and run into molds, Macock fingered the fragrant woods that were to be built into cases for clocks. The woods and orchards about Guilford gave many of the logs; cherry, apple, oak, and laurel. Cherry wood was tough and fine-grained enough to be used for wheels. Sometimes Ebenezer carved and sawed a wooden clock face, which he enameled and painted in a fair design. When a clipper ship returned with a cargo of tea and spices and rare woods from the Indies, Ebenezer would hasten to Boston to buy some mahogany logs for his clock frames. All these woods, pungent and aromatic, scented the shop and thrilled the apprentice boy, Macock.

Two shadows darkened the threshold. Abel ceased his hammering and saw Macock. He motioned for him to hide in the case of a tall clock that stood like an open coffin in a corner. The two men, talking so earnestly that neither noticed Macock's hurried disappearance, came in. One, in tall hat and long broadcloth cloak, was a selectman of Guilford. The other, in linsey-woolsey and leather apron, bone-rimmed spectacles and with work-hardened hands, was the apprentice boys' master, Ebenezer Parmele. They were talking about the town clock which Ebenezer had been commissioned to make.

"A new steeple and bell are to be added to the meeting-house, Master Ebenezer," the selectman was saying, "so it seems fitting that we commission you to make a clock to hang in the steeple, with a hammer to strike on the great bell, providing that the charge of purchasing said clock can be raised by public contributions. You would be expected to wind the clock, no matter what the weather, and keep it in repair."

Ebenezer bowed and then rubbed his hands together in pleased satisfaction. "I shall be honored to make the clock," he replied. "It shall be of brass, well-hammered and nicely decorated——" There was a sudden crash and the selectman jumped. Down to the floor in a corner fell a partly finished clock case, and out of it appeared a much terrified boy, Macock. He had leaned too far forward as he listened from his hiding place. Rubbing his head and flushed with embarrassment, Macock faced his master. Abel giggled and tried to cover his laughter with hammering. What would happen to Macock?

But nothing at all happened until the business of the town clock was finished, and Ebenezer had bowed the selectman out of the shop. Then he returned and sternly motioned Macock to stand in front of him. "What is the meaning of this disobedience, boy?" he demanded. "Have you forgotten that the term of your service as my servant is not over by many months? Do you not know that you are forbidden to enter this shop except as you tend the forge and the bellows?"

Tears filled Macock's eyes. After all, he was but a lad of twelve years. "I know, master," he said. "I ask your pardon. Send me home to my parents in disgrace if you will, but remember how I desire to use my hands with tools as Abel, your nephew, does. I want to shape the wheels of the meeting-house clock. I know I can hammer a clock face and shape the hands as well as Abel."

Ebenezer, the master craftsman, looked with more sympathy at the apprentice. He realized that he had showed favoritism in putting Abel so soon at the anvil. He wanted his good name to go down in the history of clock-making in the new land, and Abel was a Parmele, his brother's son. Theirs was an honored craft, brought to America with the English and Dutch silversmiths and engravers. He, the Guilford master craftsman, was apart from all the other clock-makers of New England in skill and resourcefulness. He had more orders than he could fill, for each clock that left his hands was perfect of its kind: smooth-running, beautiful in its carved or painted figures, and a time-keeper that would outlive him. But more than a proud craftsman, Ebenezer was an honest man. He wondered if he had been perfectly fair to this lad, whose hands longed to handle tools. Might he not be keeping back a workman who would excel himself?

Still, he frowned. "Do you mind, Macock, what it means when an apprentice disobeys his master, and is sent back to his parents, with no bag of tools or any certificate of time well spent?"

"Yes, sir, his parents are also disgraced," Macock said, "and no other trade will take him. He has no work."

"And having no work is the greatest sorrow that can come to a youth," Ebenezer reminded him.

"Yes," Macock answered, rubbing his eyes.

Abel, too, was on the point of tears. He looked pleadingly at Uncle Ebenezer.

"That would be a misfortune, for a boy who started with Ebenezer Parmele to take to the road with no trade," the clock-maker said, his face slowly changing its stern expression for a smile. He reached in the great pocket of his apron and took from it a small, beautifully formed hammer, the wooden handle as smooth as satin from usage, and the steel head gleaming like silver. He held it for a moment as if he loved it. "This was given me by my master, Bogardus, the clock-maker of New York," he told the boys. "True hammering is a great qualification in our trade and it happens that, after a long time, the skill of our hands is transferred to the tools with which we work. Not that I discredit hand skill," he warned them, "but a good man makes a good tool, and this hammer is one of the best of its kind." He held it out to Macock Ward. "Take this hammer, lad, and work beside Abel at the anvil. After today, I will get another servant to wait on your mistress and tend the fires."

So Macock Ward, at twelve years, began to make clocks in old Connecticut. As he held the little hammer in his hands, he was as happy and proud as a boy of today with his airplane model grasped in eager fingers. Bent low over the tiny brass wheels that he sawed and hammered, Macock saw in a dream the kitchen clocks, school clocks, tower clocks, ships' clocks that he would make. He decided to learn every part of the trade, which would take many years of work.

This was the period before any parts of clocks were brought to our country from Europe. The early clock-maker was our first mechanical engineer, and the old clocks were more beautiful than the ones made now. That is why some of the timepieces which went out proudly from the shops of

Connecticut are now treasured with even more pride in the art museums of our great cities.

Lantern clocks, with delicately carved tops of open-work. Clocks with engraved or colored dials on which were shown the fancies of the maker: the moon and stars, butterflies, shells, flowers, ferns, and birds in beautiful, delicately wrought designs. Tall clocks, with polished brass pendulums that swung to and fro, back and forth with the hours until the owner, with a great handmade key, wound them for another eight days' ticking. Clock cases carved of seasoned wood with pillars, hammered-brass hinges, and delicate paneling. The owner of one of the clocks Macock was helping to make was likely to be an important man of the town. In all Guilford there were only about thirty-five wooden clocks and fifty-four brass ones.

Sometimes as they worked, Master Ebenezer would tell the apprentices stories of his own boyhood. He had lived on a farm there in Guilford, and everything that was needed—cloth, plows, furniture, food—were made by his father and mother. Going to New York to learn his trade had been his dream, but first it was necessary for him to cut the timber and build the boat in which he sailed there.

"Now this clock for the meeting-house must be made, to the smallest screw, by hand," he would say. And it was.

Macock worked from sunrise to sunset. He had two suits of clothes a year, one for the shop and one to wear to church. He had no books, no games, no time for play. Although his parents lived in Wallingford, not far from Guilford, he never had a holiday to go home and see them. The years were as unvaried for him as for his clocks, except that the clocks had great days, once in a while, when one was bought and went with glory to a farmhouse or a public building. But Macock was happy. He loved the flaming of the fire beneath the glowing crucible, the perfume of wood shavings, the tap-tap of his hammer, and the ticking of the clocks. Time was going on. Ebenezer was growing old and Macock was growing tall. He would have a great trust to carry out into the world when his apprenticeship was up.

One day, we find out from old papers, something exciting happened in Wallingford. A new shop was opened. "Macock Ward, Clock-Maker," the sign read. Inside, with a precious kit of tools and a paper of good conduct from the well-known clock-maker of Guilford, Ebenezer Parmele, Macock Ward set up in business for himself. From the first he was successful, and it was noticed that he laid great store by a little, smoothly worn hammer which he never allowed any apprentice to use.

Before long, he was commissioned to make a town clock for Wallingford, which was not going to be outdone in the matter by Guilford. The record of this clock is written thus: "The town of Wallingford gives liberty to Macock Ward to sett a clok in ye steeple; and if any damadge to ye belfre, hee will pay it and taik away ye clok."

Macock Ward made and placed the clock in the belfry of his home town, and it lasted longer than the steeple. We read that he was a very clever clock-maker. He made tower clocks, made both brass and wooden tall ones, and like his master, he carved and joined the wooden cases himself. He mended pewter and brass for the neighbors, built a little furniture, and made buttons, which were just beginning to be in great demand for the uniforms of soldiers. He bought a near-by farm which he cultivated after his shop was closed for the day. It is said that the villagers of Wallingford were astounded one day by the sight of a strange vehicle coming down the tree-shaded main street. It was a one-horse chaise with wheels about five feet high. On the driver's seat of this, the first pleasure vehicle in our country, sat Macock Ward. He drove the length of the town and out into the countryside. The people along his route were amazed to hear a bell ring at the end of every mile that Macock covered. He had invented the first speedometer, a crude mechanical device underneath the buggy that rang the bell. Macock Ward was now a great man. His neighbors selected him to serve in the General Assembly.

But long after his shop had closed its doors for the last time and his one-horse chaise had dropped to pieces, Macock's clocks ticked on. Treasured and guarded, they tick today, telling of the patient skill of a little boy apprentice, and the lost art of the old clock-makers.

THE SILVERSMITH'S ADVENTURE

PAUL, TRUANT from the grammar school of Master John
Tileston on North Bennett Street in old Boston, heard a shrill
whistle. He knew who it was, his friend Crispus Attucks, a
ragged, friendly boy of the streets who led Paul into mischief whenever he could and who knew every corner of the
town from Long Wharf to Frog Pond, from Cornhill to the
North End. Half-Indian was Crispus, and half-Negro, and
his school was all outdoors. Paul Revere's father, the gold-
smith of the North End, did not approve of Paul's adventures
with Crispus. Paul should of course have been in school, but
it was the day for the spelling match and young Paul was a
very poor speller. But not a boy could excel him when Master

View of Boston from a Paul Revere Engraving

Tileston got out his plummet and rule for the drawing class.

Twelve years old was Paul, stocky, round-cheeked, his face honest in every line and showing the marks of good breeding. His father had been a French Huguenot, and Paul's dark eyes showed his French ancestry. The Revere family were well thought of in Boston of that time, about the year 1747. They lived over the shop in the North End where, with fine tools, metals, and skillful fingers Paul's father turned out the beautiful silverware for which he was famed. The North End of Boston was the craftsmen's section. There, along its narrow and twisted streets, silversmiths, shipbuilders, the carvers who shaped figureheads for ships, rope- and sailmakers, potters—all the handworkers whose crafts were needed in the growing seaport town of Boston—had their shops and plied their trades.

Paul knew that it would not be safe for him and Crispus to take their way in the direction of the North End. Crispus, indeed, would want to go farther away from the sober business of Boston.

There he was, grinning, as dark as the ancestors from whom he was descended, hardly a whole piece to his worn breeches, his jacket out at the elbows.

"Did the master see you leave?" he asked, lounging up to Paul.

"Not he," Paul boasted. "If he misses me in the spelling line, it will be near the foot, in which he is not interested. I am beginning my apprenticeship in my father's shop, and it is quite likely that Master Tileston will fancy that I am kept at home to draw a wreath of flowers for a silver pitcher, or shape the handle of a porringer. Master Tileston says that I have a knack with my fingers and should grow up to be a good silversmith," Paul said, looking down at the path, for he was a little ashamed of his role as a runaway.

"Keep up your courage, Paul," Crispus urged him. "It is too fine a day to waste in a musty school listening to a row of milksops drone out their spelling lesson. On, to the Long Wharf! I heard that a ship flying the British flag is at anchor there, waiting for this evening to spirit away some of our Boston workmen. Whether they will be taken to England or the Indies is not known, but they will never return to Boston. Come, Paul, run!"

Side by side, the boys made their way toward Long Wharf.

Boston in those days was a little town of low buildings, wide fields, and gardens. Where the Back Bay section of fine houses is now, there were then great low-lying salt marshes. Where the Common is now, there was a swath of meadowland with grazing cows, and banks of wild roses grew along the edge of Frog Pond. The Town House and Market Place saw most of the business of the Colonies transacted, for Boston was our most important seaport. Long Wharf, the goal of Crispus and Paul, was crowded with barrels, boxes, drying fish, nets, and rough seamen. Stately ships rode at anchor. It was said that colonists were taken unwillingly every voyage for work in England and her other possessions. Already there was a murmur of protest among the colonists, and the word "freedom" was on the lips of many.

The boys followed alleys and byways, edged beneath the great trees that lined the lanes, and talked together of the doings on the waterfront.

"I saw a pirate ship at anchor, far out," Crispus said in an excited whisper. "A skull and crossbones was painted on her flag, and the crew, sitting at supper in the tavern, wore gold earrings."

"Think you," asked Paul, "that we shall get a look at those big pistols they carry in their belts? I feel like a pirate captain myself, when I stand on the end of Long Wharf and smell the sea and look off to where water and land join."

They had almost reached the wharf—a turn of a winding street would bring them there—when Paul suddenly stopped. Turning the corner, a little girl came toward them. Although she was dressed like the other Boston children in a long calico dress, an apron, a cape, and a bonnet tied demurely under her chin, this little maid was as pretty as any fairy. The close-fitting bonnet could not keep her curls within its rim. Her small feet in their stoutly pegged shoes fairly twinkled along the cobblestones.

"Here comes your friend, Sarah Orne," said Crispus, darting down an alley. "I'll leave you here."

Brought face to face with Paul, whose cheeks had grown ruddy with shame, Sarah pointed an accusing finger at him.

"Paul Revere, I never thought to find you here, when school is keeping," she accused him. "Perhaps Master Tileston has sent you on an errand?"

Paul's face flushed a deeper crimson. "I heard Crispus whistle, and so I joined him," he explained. "It was the spelling hour, and I knew I should play the dunce. Listening to the wind in the sails is more to my liking, or," he added, "hammering a fine pattern on a silver ewer or a mug."

"But you must go to school if you are going to be your father's apprentice, Paul," Sarah told him. "And Crispus Attucks is no good companion for you, as you very well know."

"But I like him," Paul explained. Sarah had turned him toward home and was walking beside him. "He knows where the best berries grow, and where to hide on the wharf and watch the ships unload. Crispus can tell stories of the days when Indians lived here. And I am sorry for him," Paul went on. "I do not know if I am soft or hard, but I melt at the sight of even a lost dog."

Sarah smiled up into Paul's honest face. She slipped her hand into his. "We will walk slowly along the river, Paul, and when it is time for school to be over, you can go home.

I will never say that I saw you playing truant with Crispus, but do not do it again."

Nothing happened to Paul Revere because he played truant from school. There was a large family of children in the Revere home, and he slipped in to supper with no one but Crispus and Sarah Orne the wiser for his day's adventure. His father, looking up from his pewter plate of cornmeal pudding, said, "I had a good report of you, Paul, from Master Tileston. He says that you draw better than any pupil in the school. In a few years now I shall perhaps give the shop into your hands. Your skill in drawing will serve you well in our craft."

Paul Revere was only sixteen years old when he left school and took his place at a bench in his father's shop. There had never been such rarely beautiful tableware, porringers, ewers, pitchers, flagons, and bowls as were turned out from this small shop in long-ago Boston. The craft of the silversmith in those days was an honored one. Machine-made, plated silver had never been heard of. The spoons, mugs, and porringers that graced the dinner tables of our colonists were all decorated and shaped with the greatest skill by hand. In this old and shining craft, young Paul was put to work.

He first learned how to weld the gold and silver that was used. Then the slender, hand-made engraving tools were put into his hands. Before long, remembering the drawing lessons he had enjoyed so much at Master Tileston's, Paul Revere began to make his own designs.

As the boy bent over his bright pieces of silver, tracing and shaping garlands of wild roses on their polished surfaces, he often heard Crispus Attucks's whistle outside in the

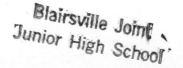

street. It was so piercing that Paul could hear it above the hammers of the shipbuilders, the sounds of all the other craftsmen of the North End, but he did not look up. Crispus's smiling face, his flying tattered sleeve, would appear at the window of the silversmith's shop, but Paul only waved a greeting. He had found something to do that was completely to his liking. He was shaping history as he molded a lovely piece of silverware.

The Revere silver began to be increasingly in demand, especially that which Paul designed. There was a quality to his pieces that even his father could not explain.

The flowing lines of marsh grasses and stems of water

Paul Revere

Copy of
Book-plate
Engraved by
Paul Revere

plants were transferred by Paul's fingers to the handles of
spoons. His father's wealthy customers insisted that no one
but he should engrave their crests and coats of arms on their
wedding silverware. Everything that Paul Revere made of
silver was shaped and turned so as to be precisely adapted to
its intended use. There had never been such useful and at
the same time decorative teapots and tankards as his. His
curved patterns were solid, strong, and bold, like the curving
waves and clouds he had watched so many times from the
Long Wharf. Silverware, to be beautiful, must be simple,
like unruffled water, so as to send out its softly polished
surfaces and reflections. Paul Revere knew this, and he made

his designs large and restrained, and polished the silver around them to a soft luster.

Finishing a set of porringers or a dozen silver spoons, Paul would pack them in saddlebags and mount his horse for the dangerous ride to deliver them. Roads were poor. There were no trains or street lights or police in those days. Carrying saddlebags heavy with silver to the villages outside Boston meant fording streams, running the gantlet of forest outlaws hiding in the deep woods along the way. He must ride far into the blackness of the night made lonely by the hooting of owls, the rustling of brush, the crackling of twigs. But Paul learned to ride fast and without fear.

Paul Revere was about thirteen years old when he began these dangerous trips on horseback. His father refused to let the boy have his pistols. "You must trust to the horse's speed, Paul," he said. So Paul would be off in the morning with the heavy saddlebags. Past the shops of the craftsmen. Up the hill to Town House. Down Cornhill. Across Frog Lane and out towards Roxbury. Then along the old Providence Road where the dangers began. Farms were far apart and he might have to go far as Dedham to deliver his silver. Before he knew it, dusk would settle down around him. A bullet might whine past him, but he would duck his head, dig his heels into the horse's sides, and ride, ride! Paul Revere could ride!

On Sundays Paul walked along the shore of the Charles River with Sarah Orne as they planned the patterns of spoons and mugs he would make for their own home when he was a little older. When Paul was nineteen he took full charge of his father's shop. Before long, Boston was the

scene of troubled times. There was a Boston massacre, and
Paul Revere's friend, Crispus Attucks, was killed.

Then came the rumor that enemy troops were creeping
by night upon Boston. Word of the proposed attack came
to Paul Revere, and once more he saddled his horse for a
midnight ride. Off he galloped, signaling and arousing the
farmers on the outskirts of Boston. We may be sure that his
boyhood rides were in Paul Revere's mind as he took his
lonely way over the same dark and hazardous roads that he
had taken with his bags of silverware as a boy. He remembered the street of the craftsmen in the old North End. How
he had drawn a wreath of wild flowers and chased the design on a polished silver bowl. How he had packed the silver.
How he had ridden off, alone, to deliver it. As Paul Revere
rode to arouse the farmers of Lexington and the surround-
ing countryside of Boston, Crispus Attucks, his boyhood
friend, rode beside him in his dreams. At the end of the ride,
he fancied that Sarah Orne might be waiting for him. When
they had grown up, she had married Paul Revere and they
had started their own silver shop in Boston. So, riding with
the wind, dreaming, holding his courage like a banner, Paul
Revere spread the alarm.

The story might stop here, but it does not. Boys and girls
have learned that the man, Paul Revere, was a patriot; but
more than that, and closer to his heart, was his craft of making beautiful things with metal. War always destroys for a
time the art of a country. So our Revolution checked the
art of our silver- and goldsmiths, but Paul Revere went on
making useful things that the colonists needed. He learned
foundry work and in the year 1792 he cast the first bell that

Boston hung on a public building. He opened his own foundry, and at his forge there were welded all the bolts, spikes, and other copper fittings that made the warship *Constitution* last until today. He cast the bell that rang for liberty on this ship, nicknamed "Old Ironsides," until it was shot away in action. He engraved and printed the first paper money of our Revolutionary Government.

In our early days, a hardware shop was a very important place. For many years Paul Revere's hardware shop supplied Boston with silverware, made buttons for uniforms, carved bracelets and gold necklaces, rings, lockets and chains, sold stockings and cloth in addition to tools, dishes, and many kinds of copperware. There, at his workbench behind the counter, Paul Revere could be found until he grew to be an old man. The painter, Gilbert Stuart, who made a name for himself through his portraits of George Washington, found Paul Revere and painted his picture. Copies of this portrait may be seen today, that of a round-faced, thickset gentleman, not tall and wearing knee breeches. Paul Revere would probably have preferred being painted in his leather apron.

But among the most valued possessions of some of our American museums today, and of a few Boston families, are the pieces of silverware that Paul Revere designed and made. His graceful garlands of flowers, carefully drawn medallions, perfectly shaped bowls, pitchers, mugs, and porringers are records of our history that far outrank the story of his ride in the night to Lexington. He was not interested in war. He cast seventy-five bells that rang from the steeples of New England churches. Paul Revere was one of the great craftsmen of our country.

THE GARDEN MERCY PLANTED

STANDING IN the door of their cabin, Mercy Harriman felt the warm spring sunshine on her face, sniffed a small arbutus-scented breeze blowing down from the hills. Her younger sister Mary, her little brother, and the baby had been fed their early supper of corn-mush and milk. The cabin was as neat as nine-year-old Mercy could sweep and scour it. She had fastened the gate of the sheepfold, for they had heard wolves crying last night. Mercy remembered her father's words as he and her mother had started away that morning.

"Take good care of the little ones, Mercy. I shall wait for this corn to be ground at the mill and your mother is going to pick out some calico at the store to make you and Mary new dresses. We shall spend the night at the miller's. Don't be lonely, daughter. We shall be home tomorrow, God willing."

Mercy had watched them start off, the bags of corn on her father's back, her mother waving her sunbonnet as they walked toward the river. The Harrimans were the first homesteaders there in Bath, New Hampshire, and they had no neighbors. There were four Indian wigwams between them and the little rippling river, the Ammonoosuc, but the Indians had not troubled the Harrimans in their year there at the foot of Gardener's Mountain where Jaasiel Harriman had built their cabin. There was no bridge across the river, but a canoe lay on the shore for anyone who needed to cross over to the mill and the general store on the other side. That had been the way Mercy and the others had come to Bath the year before, 1766, from their first home in Concord. They were a family of Puritans, come to the land of promise from Yorkshire in England. Mercy, resting there in the cabin door, remembered their pilgrimage.

They had walked through the wilderness from Concord to Bath. First her father, driving the pair of oxen and carrying bags of grain on his back. Then her mother carrying the baby and leading the little boy. Then Mercy holding Mary's hand. An old hunter had guided them through the forest. It was four days' hard trailing from Concord. When they reached the river, Jaasiel had let the children and their mother ride over the ford on the backs of the oxen. He held the oxen's heads as they splashed through the water. They had all been afraid when they passed by the four Indian wigwams between them and the meadows, but had seen nothing.

Jaasiel Harriman was now an important man, the first proprietor of Bath, because he had built the first cabin there. Other settlers would soon be on their way to this fertile little valley, with the sky-tops of the White Mountains on the east, and the friendly Green Mountains at the west. The red loam of the rich earth oozed fertility. One of the laws of the Colony was that a new settler might have free title to his land if he planted and tended five acres for every fifty acres of land he took up; otherwise he would forfeit his claim. Mercy knew about that law. She knew that her father had not kept it. But it had been a hard first year for them all.

For a while they had no meal. Mercy's mother had pounded the grain into flour for their bread on flat stones. They had all camped out under the shelter of a hill until Jaasiel could cut logs and build their cabin. Jaasiel had brought no seeds with him, and they had no plow. All these matters would be straightened out next year, Mercy knew, but as she looked across at the hills already turning rosy with the blossoms of the maple trees, as she sniffed the sweetness of wild flowers, she was suddenly frightened. Suppose one of the stern Puritan dictators of the period should ride into Bath on horseback and discover that the Harrimans had done no planting! Suppose they should all be driven away, to follow another footpath into the wilderness! Mercy wrung her small work-hardened hands.

She went inside the cabin and knelt before the small chest covered with horsehair in which the family kept their poor possessions. She touched them with tender fingers. A New England speller. Her mother's Paisley shawl. Mary's best doll with a china head and a bright calico dress. Some bay-

berry candles she and her mother had made last winter. And from underneath these Mercy pulled out a small calico bag that she had made. She opened it.

In the bag were some seeds that she had saved. Pumpkin seeds, big, flat, and white. Kernels of the best corn saved from the grinding. Some seeds of cucumbers that she had allowed to grow yellow and go to seed, although her mother had wanted to make the cucumbers into pickles.

Once in a long time a farmer with baskets of vegetables rode by and the Harrimans bought from him. Perhaps, Mercy thought, her father would buy seeds on this trip he had taken to the mill. But she had a plan of her own for planting the seeds that she had saved. She tied the bag again and slipped it into its hiding place in the chest. Now, she decided, was a good time to find a plot for her garden. She went out of the cabin door, and a little way toward the river. Then she stopped breathing with terror. From the four Indian wigwams there came four savages, painted red from top to toe. Slinking through the bushes, crawling through the tall grass of the meadow, they came on steadily and swiftly towards the Harrimans' cabin.

Only for a second of fear was Mercy powerless. As she raced back, her mind kept pace with her flying feet. Of course the Indians had seen her father and mother pass by that morning on their way across the river. They must have been biding their attack for months, as savages sometimes did. They would be safe from capture with only four children at home. It would be easy for them to steal, to murder.

Mary, being alone, had taken her doll out of the chest and sat in her little red rocking chair, singing to it. Mercy put her hand over her little sister's mouth, then lifted and pushed her into a barrel of goose feathers in a corner. She whispered to the little boy not to speak, and hid him underneath their washtub, with a trailing quilt hanging down to conceal him. Another quilt hung across a corner of the cabin to partition off a room. Back of this curtain Mercy hid with the baby, giving him a lump of precious maple sugar to keep him quiet. She peered out through a fold of the quilt as the four red-painted shadows came down the path, crossed the door-sill, and entered.

They looked like four great redbirds, their head feathers flapping, their scarlet blankets waving like gigantic wings. They peered under the bed built of logs against the wall, pulled out the children's trundle bed, poked menacing fingers into the curtain of Mercy's hiding place. Then they

found a brace of wild partridges that Jaasiel had shot and hung over the fireplace ready for tomorrow's dinner. The Indians clutched at the fowl, thrust them into the embers of the fire, then tore them apart, eating them fairly raw.

Mary, buried in the feathers, sneezed. Mercy stopped breathing in terror, but the Indians had not heard. The quilt that covered the little brother's hiding place underneath the washtub trembled with his fear. Suppose, Mercy thought, the baby should cry for more sugar! But he went contentedly to sleep, one chubby sugary thumb in his mouth. The Indians moved about stealthily, investigating corners and shelves. Mercy was now completely gripped with terror. It would be only a few moments before the Indians found their hiding places. Scalping, killing, kidnaping by savages were not tales in Mercy's life; they were everyday happenings.

Suddenly the savages discovered the chest which was still open. They poured out the contents upon the floor. One tried on Mistress Harriman's shawl; no, he decided that he preferred his blanket. They opened the little bag of seeds but discarded that too. The bayberry candles they liked. They divided them, and without a sound left the cabin as silently as they had come.

Mercy laid the baby in the trundle bed, lifted choking Mary from the barrel of feathers, and pulled the boy from beneath the washtub. Warning them all to be still, she crept to the door. The Indians were going home in single file, a line of crimson against the green of the spring-meadow. One of them turned and waved a friendly hand back toward the cabin. Perhaps, Mercy thought, their red paint had been their calling costume. Perhaps, having waited a year for the Harrimans to make them a visit, they had decided to pay the first call themselves. A brace of partridges and a few candles, Mercy thought, mattered very little in comparison with the bag of seeds the Indians had left behind. As she put the younger children to bed that night, Mercy decided that she would not wait another day before planting her garden.

The sun was as warm, the breeze as fragrant, the next morning as if the day before had not come so close to tragedy. Mercy decided that a hollow on the hill beneath which their cabin stood would be the best place for the garden. With wooden spoons she and the others dug up the rich red loam of the meadow. Then she carried the earth up the hill in her apron until in the hollow there was a rich little plot for the seeds.

Mercy planted the kernels of corn, and blessed them with an old rhyme as she dropped them in the holes:

> One for the blackbird.
> One for the crow.
> One for the cutworm,
> And two to grow.

She planted the pumpkin seeds where they would rise in the autumn in great golden balls at the foot of the cornstalks. She planted the cucumber seeds where the vines would have plenty of space to spread. And with every apronful of earth, with every seed, nine-year-old Mercy Harriman planted a village of gardens, a village of white homes, fields of grain, and orchards heavy with fruit.

She had just finished her planting when Jaasiel and Mistress Harriman came home. Jaasiel carried bags of meal, ground at the mill; Mistress Harriman had a bundle of pink and blue calico for new dresses for her little daughters. The father and mother, when they learned what Mercy had done, were proud of their little daughter and happy that they now had a garden.

The garden that Mercy Harriman planted in Bath in the year 1767 grew and spread. Soon other settlers came and built homes, planted and tended other gardens. In the year 1808 something exciting happened in Bath. A traveling peddler brought the first clock to the village. Its long pendulum swung with the days and seasons of planting and harvesting. In the year 1811, another event occurred. Jaasiel Harriman bought and drove proudly home along the Bath turnpike, the first wagon. Stoutly built, Jaasiel Harriman's

wagon carried between field and barn the great loads of
corn, the plump pumpkins that had grown from the seed
of Mercy's first garden. Her garden was bright with flowers
by that year: golden marigolds, zinnias of every tint of red,
orange, and yellow, clove pinks so sweet that their perfume
was like a wave carried along the summer air, bravely
blooming asters and dahlias that lasted until frost came.

And in the year 1816, when Mercy Harriman was only
a memory, the first stove came by stagecoach to the village
of Bath. Sitting around it one cold winter evening in the
village store, recalling the season so long before when Jaasiel
Harriman drove his oxen into Bath and built his cabin, some
of the landholders decided to build a fence about the little
hollow in the hill where Mercy Harriman had planted the
first garden. Bath was then a town; it had an upper and a
lower village, and fertile farms spread out their checkerboard
of green where the wigwams of Indians had stood. There
was a bridge across the river. White frame houses, churches,
a school, stores straggling along the Main Street dreamed of
the days when Mercy carried earth in her apron up the hill.

So it was decided that this little girl's garden site should
be marked. An iron fence was built and on a high bowlder

near Mercy's garden plot the people of Bath placed a tablet that read:

"This tablet marks the site of the first garden in Bath in 1767. Earth was carried in her apron to the top of this rock by Mercy Harriman, nine-year-old daughter of Jaasiel Harriman. Near by was his cabin."

New England through the years planted the most beautiful gardens of all the earth. Poppies, white candytuft, pink and blue morning glories that hung their bells from trailing vines, roses that spread from doorways to every roadside, blue larkspur, tall hollyhocks, gay nasturtiums, flaming tiger lilies bloomed everywhere. Wild lovely arbutus, blue gentian, pink clover, buttercups, and daisies filled the meadows with color. The flowers of New England perfumed the old rooms. Rose petals folded themselves away in drawers of linen, or filled china jars with spicy potpourri. They always went to church and to a wedding. They drew their shapes and painted their colors on hooked rugs, on chintzes and china. They made wreaths on painted furniture and gave the great cabinet-makers designs for carving.

Seeds, roots, and bulbs were hoarded from one season to the next, to bloom in richer colors with each new planting. Vast seed-houses were founded, built on the precious seedlings of New England gardens. Flower-shows, visited by millions, are given every winter where the gardens of yesterday blossom again indoors for the people of the skyscrapers. So from the earth that Mercy carried up her hill to our gardens of today, there is a story-road, bright and fragrant, for us to follow.

THE BOY WHO LOVED TOOLS

THERE WAS very little furniture in the turf cottage in Loch Fannich, Scotland, where the Phyfe family lived. The boy Duncan opened his eyes in a wooden cradle in 1768, and as he grew older and able to set his feet on the earthen floor, his first steps took him from an old carved chest to a stool, from there to a rude deal table. The Phyfes had little else except the straw beds. But when Duncan grew to be a boy old enough to cross the threshold of the cottage, he found all the world of moor and hill and forest waiting to be explored.

Gabel Phyfe, the father of Duncan and his brothers and sisters, was a Scottish herdsman. Soon the boy Duncan was given a flock to tend. Following the sheep and lambs about their rocky pastures, he became well acquainted with the wind-swept trees, the waving grasses, the fields of purple heather and bluebells. Wrapped in a cloak of the Mackenzie plaid, the clan to which the Phyfe family belonged, Duncan stood on the top of a hill, looking toward the horizon beyond which lay the sea. He wondered if he and the sheep would always spend their days together, if he would follow them home to their fold and eat his supper and bannocks and porridge every night in Loch Fannich until he grew to be a man. A boy of even those long-ago days dreamed, and by way of a Highland regiment word had come of a new land across the ocean, a land where English, Scotch, French, and Dutch had voyaged to build new homesteads and look for fortune.

Coming slowly down the hill pasture, gathering together the straying sheep with the help of his great shaggy dog, Duncan started home through the sunset. He went slowly, for there was no need of haste. He knew that home, the cottage with its candlelight, the night of stars, and tomorrow's shepherding would be no different from all his past. But before he had fastened the gate of the sheepfold, the boy knew that something had happened. The shrill sound of bagpipes came from the bench outside the cottage where a visiting soldier sat in kilts and tartan. Duncan's mother was busy packing the carved chest with the family's clothes. His father was counting the coins in his money bag. The younger children met Duncan with shining eyes and cheeks rosy with excitement.

"Father has sold the flock," they told him. "This man

from the regiment has told us of a new town in America, Albany, on the great Hudson River, where there are other Scottish people. We are leaving Scotland to find our fortunes in the new land."

The next few months were like Duncan's dream come true, but with unexpected hardships. There was the long trip by wagon, with their goods, to the seaport. The long voyage in a small sailing ship to New York took nearly all of Gabel Phyfe's money. The trip was stormy and hard to bear. Little Eliza Phyfe died at sea. When they reached the new land and started on a second journey by wagon trail and boat up the Hudson to Albany, the Phyfe family wondered if they had not been following a rainbow. Fortune seemed very far away. But they found the Albany of the year 1784 a thriving town of little brick-and-stone houses, snowy hills where a boy could coast as far down as the river, and plenty of work for men and boys who knew how to use their hands.

One of the thriving trades of Albany was the building of carts and wagons. Commercial business had begun, and farm produce, flour, furs, clothing, bricks had to be taken up and down the river, along the trails or by boat. The dock at Albany was crowded with carts. Roads going west were being rutted by great lumbering Conestoga wagons, big enough to hold an entire family, their goods, and food for the long journey into the unexplored wilderness of the prairie country. It seemed best to bind out Duncan Phyfe to a wagoner in Albany from whom he could learn about the different kinds of wood, and how to shape an axle and fit together the spokes of a wheel. It might lead to a knowledge of joinery, a good trade, one of the best. Duncan went to work almost as soon as the Phyfes reached Albany.

Duncan was about fifteen years old then. Because his father soon died and the rest of the family scattered, there was urgent need of his learning a trade. One can picture this boy handling, planing, carving wood in a pleasant old wagon shop during the term of his apprenticeship. The smell of pungent wood, varnish, and paints mingled with that of the fruit trees outside and the flowers in the Dutch gardens. Soon Duncan was helping to make coaches in which the rich folk of Albany would ride down to New York for the social events that followed the election of George Washington as our first president. The trade of coach-making in our growing country was an art, and the Scotch became leaders in it. Coach doors and windows were decorated with carving, and the boy, bending over his work-bench, found that the designs he had known as a shepherd lad, wild flowers, leaves, shells, the stars at night, and the slender, moving branches of trees were coming to life in wood under his skilled fingers and his carving tools.

So, carving, mixing glue, fitting and joining, polishing, dreaming, Duncan's apprenticeship was at last over. His brother John was driving one of the new horse-drawn omnibuses that carried people about in New York. Then, as now, this growing city lying on the great harbor lured young people. Duncan Phyfe packed his most precious possession, his tool-chest, and set out to walk to New York. When he could get a little repairing or furniture-making along the shore of the Hudson, he was able to earn his board and lodging. Sometimes he slept in the meadows or woods along the

way, remembering the days when he was a shepherd lad. Duncan was young, but he had a plan for his life. He was going to New York to try to put this plan into action.

New York was a town of craftsmen. Our country was still new enough for there to be an ever-growing need of carry-alls, furniture, casks, crates, cloth, bricks, boards, all the necessities of living and going about. John Jacob Astor, the fur prince of New York, had started big business and was now very wealthy. Shipbuilding, trade with the Indies, the building of fine furniture by hand were making New York very prosperous. Broad Street, near the water, was the street of the joiners. Here great planks of rare woods were brought from the ships, or from the forest lards of the North and the Jersey shore.

Within the shops, the pieces of furniture that were then in demand were shaped at the bench, on the lathe, and in the hands of the craftsmen. Making highboys and lowboys, those beautiful chests of drawers that were then in fashion; Windsor chairs, four-poster beds, desks, tables, chests, sofas, marked our growing prosperity. American homes were being furnished almost as beautifully as those which the colonists had left in England and France. A share in this craft seemed to cottage-born Duncan Phyfe a wonderful career.

We hear of him first in his own little joiner's shop at 2 Broad Street. He worked modestly and by hand. He never put his name in the newspapers as the other furniture-makers of Broad Street did, nor did Duncan Phyfe carve his name on his pieces in the manner of the times. Designed and built by himself, from the forest wood to the finished chest of drawers or sofa, strong enough to last hundreds of years, fair enough to find a place in a museum of art today, well enough made with only his hands and his tools to suit a great craftsman, Duncan Phyfe's furniture was from the first something to be proud of. He fitted all the parts together with great skill. The legs were sometimes given claws and winged carvings. Leaves like those of the trees from which his chests, chairs, and tables were made were carved in the wood for decorations. Flowing curves like the lines of the clouds on a shepherd's hill, bits of shaped brass shining like the sun, skillfully molded chair backs like lyres, special bands and panels of grained veneer that showed off to the best effect the style of a desk or highboy marked Duncan Phyfe's furniture. But still he worked alone in his small shop and wore the old beaver hat he had brought from Albany, not troubling to make a show like his neighboring craftsmen.

One day a very fine coach drove down Broad Street and stopped near Duncan's shop. In flowered bonnet and silk mantle, out stepped the newly married daughter of the rich Mr. Astor, the fur merchant. Her name was Mrs. Langdon, and she was a great beauty of old New York. She was looking for furniture for her new house, and she stopped at the door of Number 2, looking in curiously at the solitary joiner. Perhaps he was stretching the last piece of brocaded damask over a long sofa with claw legs and tiny curled rosettes at the back like the curved horns of one of his Scottish rams. Perhaps he was putting the last brass leaf against the front of a dark, polished highboy. Perhaps he was fitting together the parts of a long banqueting table that could be made large or small at will. The stories do not tell just what it was in Duncan Phyfe's modest shop that attracted the beautiful and rich Mrs. Langdon, but with a rustle of crinoline and a cry of delight, she was across his threshold.

"I must have this. . . . I want that. . . . Could you furnish my whole house?"

Duncan Phyfe was dazed, dumb. All he had been trying to do was to make strong, useful, beautiful furniture and here he was, famous at the turn of a coach's wheels and the opened purse of a lovely lady.

It amused the daughter of Mr. Astor to take her friends to see the tiny shop of this dour Scotch craftsman, who sometimes forgot to take off his old beaver hat when they rushed in upon him, and who would never be hurried in his work. It became the fashion to have as much of Duncan Phyfe's furniture in one's house as possible, and at last he

found it necessary to take in some apprentices and build a new shop. Then he built himself a house and a storage warehouse, and all of these buildings were as plain and beautiful as his handcraft. They stood side by side on old Partition Street in New York. After Robert Fulton took his steamboat successfully up the Hudson River, Partition Street was renamed Fulton Street. If you should go to New York today, remember that the great Hudson Terminal is on the site of Duncan Phyfe's Partition Street shop, warehouse, and home.

Success had come to the Scotch shepherd boy. He always made his own drawings and plans, but soon he was employing his brother Lochlin, whom he sent to England for fine brass. He engaged a large number of joiners, carvers, and polishers. He met the clipper ships on the waterfront which brought him the finest of Santo Domingo and Cuban mahogany for his lumber yard. In far-away tropic ports the term "Phyfe logs" became known, for Mr. Phyfe would pay one thousand dollars for one log if sound and well-grained. Philadelphia, Albany, the new towns of New Jersey, as well as New York, furnished markets for Duncan Phyfe's furniture. He was designing and building American furniture as it had not been made before, and soon his craft made him an unusually rich man for those days.

But the very few records of Duncan Phyfe which we have depict him as always busy, modest, and retiring. Although his sofas, chairs, and tables bring fabulous prices now, and a long banqueting table he made has a place of great honor in the Metropolitan Museum of Art in New York, Mr. Phyfe seldom took the trouble to sign his pieces and so much of his work is lost. Designing and finishing his hand-some, delicately carved pieces was his great reward, and until he was an old man he could be seen daily consulting with his apprentices or bent over his own bench executing a rosette or shaping a bit of brass.

After a while the sign above the shop read, "Duncan Phyfe & Son." If a grown person wanted to see the great Duncan himself, he had a hard time, but children knew the way to his garden. In a little shop he had built at one end of his garden, a small, plump old Scotch gentleman could be found at his bench, busily making sewing-tables for little girls, boxes to hold ribbons and beads, cradles and chests of drawers for dolls. These he would give away to good children. Mr. Phyfe had about half a million dollars in the bank, but what he still valued most was his tool-chest and the feeling of a bit of wood in his fingers.

CHRISTMAS SHIP

As GEORGE LEE and his best friend Amy approached the waterfront, the summer perfumes of sun-drenched honeysuckle and roses were drowned in the fragrant scent of the wood the shipbuilders were sawing and carving. The little shops along Essex Street of old Salem, Massachusetts, into which they peered, window-shopping for rock candy and cinnamon sticks, gave way to those of the ship-chandlers. Here were the sailmakers, who sat cross-legged on long tables, stitching tough canvas with thimbles fastened in the middle of their palms. Here stood the warehouses where ships' cargoes were stored, and the counting houses where bills of lading for the merchant ships were written and money was paid and taken in.

It was the year 1786, and the ships of Salem, built in the yards along the wharves, were famous in all the ports of the world. Amy was the daughter of a Salem merchant, and George was the twelve-year-old son of Captain Thomas Lee of that town. The two liked nothing better than to watch the workmen in Captain Enos Briggs's shipyard, toward which they were now heading—a boy in sailor blue and a girl in flowered calico, children born beside, and lovers of, the sea.

Meeting the pungent odors that flowed from the wharves, Amy tilted her small nose and sniffed delightedly. "I sat for an hour in father's office yesterday on his high stool, reading the ships' bills at his desk," she told George. "Oh, but the ports our ships touch must be curious! China, for example."

"My mother's blue Canton tea set, with cups like big bowls, and the sugar jar with a silver boar's head for a handle, came from China," George said.

"And my Canton beads," added Amy. "They are made, father said, of dull blue clay, but there is silver sprinkled in each bead like star dust. They have a strong sweet perfume when I wear them."

"And my Chinese picture book," George said, "made of rice paper, with little mandarins walking in blue and yellow in the sky, above the heads of jugglers tossing yellow balls and ladies carrying colored umbrellas!"

"My grandmother has a great Canton sweetmeat jar, blue china with a cover of silver and filled with preserved ginger," Amy boasted. "And my father ordered a Chinese shawl last year for mother; it is of white silk with lilies embroidered in silver. She has another shawl too, a scarlet camel's-hair one covered all over with a pattern of yellow palm leaves."

"The camel's-hair shawl came from Arabia, I venture to say," George explained, "along with a cargo of coffee, gum copal, dates, ivory, and hemp."

"Think of the Indies!" Amy sighed. "I visit them when I listen to the screaming of my little green parrot or taste our guava jelly spread on a muffin for tea."

"India burns my tongue with the hot curry powder my father likes mixed so heavily in his rice and chicken," George said laughing. "He knows islands where monkeys live like people in the forests, and where black tamarinds grow. Sugar and indigo come from the Indies. From Italy he brings home salt and figs, raisins, lemons, and rare woods."

"It is said," Amy went on, smacking her lips, "that the ship *Belisarius* once brought ten thousand pounds of rock candy to Salem from Calcutta. Well, here we are at Captain Briggs's shipyard. Do you think that we may go in, George?"

"Only if we hide," George told her. "Children are not welcome here, for they meddle with the blocks of wood and the shavings. But this is the noon hour and the yard is empty. Quick! We will play among the figureheads until the carvers return from their dinner."

They slipped inside the gate of the shipyard, ran past the great frameworks of half-built ships, past the long masts, the litter of tools, chips, logs, and planks, until they came to a part of the yard that looked like a scene from a wonder tale. There stood a wooden Indian; beside the Indian was a Scotch Highlander in kilts, playing his bagpipes with wooden hands. A carved angel with a trumpet had been covered with precious gold leaf. Neptune, ruler of the ocean, towered above a Salem witch. George Washington stood between a great wooden eagle and a dolphin. A group of saints waited apart in one corner of the little street of the carvers.

The children went up and down among the figureheads, touching their wonderfully carved forms with reverence. Designed by seafarers, hand-tooled to the smallest feather and lock of hair, no ship sailed from Salem without one. The figurehead, fastened to the ship's bow, was the vessel's guide and protector, taking her safely to port through calm and storm.

"I am sure I could carve if I had the chance," George said. He picked up a block of the solid white oak that the carvers used, and began to draw upon it with a piece of chalk. "The out-standing parts like this arm, a trumpet, Neptune's trident, a spear, or George Washington's sword, are carved separately. They are made to screw onto the figure so that they can be unscrewed at sea and taken off if there is a bad storm. They are put on again when the vessel rides into port.

"You have to get the rake of the ship's bow," he went on. "Then you set up your block of wood so that when you finish your carving the figurehead will fit in with the general rake of the stern, and the vessel's fore-and-aft lines."

"You are clever, George," Amy said. She was posed beside a tall figurehead with flowing draperies and a wreath of laurel on the long hair.

"Oh, so-so!" George replied, watching Amy out of the corner of his eye as he continued to draw.

The salt air, the half-alive figures that surrounded the boy and girl, wove a magic spell. They felt themselves skimming blue waves at the bow of a ship, leaving the little home town

of Salem behind, rolling into a horizon beyond which lay the wonder places whose names were familiar to them. Zanzibar, Calcutta, Singapore, Madrid—would the flying figurehead take them safely there and home again?

Amy, leaning against the figure, dreamed silently. George, his chalk drawing finished, took up a sharp knife from among the carving tools the workmen had left and cut into the white, grained surface of the block of wood. It had been an hour, although a short one, when a warning sound startled the children. In through the shipyard gate streamed the workmen. A firm hand on George's shoulder made him drop his knife and look up a little defiantly. Captain Enos Briggs himself, one of the great among old Salem's seafarers and the proprietor of the shipyard, shook the boy violently.

"Meddling again, you young rascal!" he shouted. "Don't you know children are forbidden here? It's even more amiss to dull a carver's sharp tools! And you the son of a sea-captain, George!"

George pulled himself loose of the captain's grip. "That is why I like your shipyard, Captain Briggs," he protested. "I want to make a figurehead to carry a fast ship to foreign parts. I can carve, if I have a little teaching and a chance at the wood."

Amy, who knew that her gay smile could charm Captain Briggs into a good humor any day, was bending over George's chalk drawing. She held it up. "Look!" she exclaimed. "George has drawn a likeness of me, but wearing a long and flowing dress, and a wreath of laurel on the hair."

Captain Briggs took the block of wood and studied the face which George had begun to carve. His weathered,

frowning countenance wrinkled into a smile. "A good likeness of Amy!" he exclaimed. "And a sure knife stroke in
the carving. You can handle a tool, George Lee." He thought
a moment. "This must be kept a secret though," he said
finally. "I doubt if the likeness of a little Salem lass ever
rode as a figurehead on the prow of a ship. But the *Juno* is
ready to launch, all but her figurehead. If you will work out
your apprenticeship honestly, George, and your father gives
his permission, you may come to work tomorrow under my
instruction, and finish your carving of young Amy here to
adorn the *Juno*."

George served his apprenticeship in wood carving well. In
those days a boy was ready to go to sea at fourteen or fifteen
years, and as George drew and painstakingly tooled the
wooden figures that were the distinguishing mark of every
vessel that sailed from Salem, he felt that he was sharing
in the vast sea trade our swift sailing vessels were establishing.
The *Juno*, with Amy's likeness carved on the figurehead, was
safely launched that year and sailed off.

Winter, spring, autumn, and another winter came to the
little town. Amy was then ten years old, and helping her
mother prepare for Christmas. It was celebrated simply in
Salem homes, but Amy was expecting George Lee to help
her with the decorations. When the rich fruit and spice
cakes were made, she planned to meet him for some holiday
shopping. George would sail away as a young seaman soon.
She knew this might be their last Christmas together.

Amy put on her fur-lined hood and cape and started out
to meet George on Essex Street. Salem might disapprove of
Christmas gayety, but not the plump little man on Essex

Street, whose shop beneath its wooden awning was like an enchanted cavern. Amy ran toward his corner. It was a Christmas bower with the evergreen wreaths, the ropes of holly, and sprays of mistletoe he had hung from the wooden awning that stretched out over the street. His name is lost to history, but the children of Salem loved this ambassador of Santa Claus. At the Christmas grotto he had made, Amy stopped dancing in delight. The plump little shopkeeper came out to greet her, rubbing his hands together in satisfaction and good cheer.

"George Lee will meet me here in a few minutes," Amy said. "He and I are going to select Christmas wreaths."

"Come in and see my stock while you wait," the shopkeeper urged her.

As they went from one candle-lighted treasure to another, Amy's eyes sparkled. Tiny bright beads sold by the thimbleful for embroidering bags. Little wooden dolls three inches high, jointed and with scarlet boots painted on their funny flat feet. Red-and-white peppermint sticks. Slabs of frosted gingerbread. Ropes of snowy popcorn. Sugar birds and animals, and braids, twists, and baskets made of pink and white sugar. Bunches of cherries made of red barley candy, with lengths of stiff yellow broom corn for stems.

"Merry Christmas!" That was all that Amy could say, as the shopkeeper laid one of the jointed wooden dolls in her mittened hands.

"But I need oranges a ship would bring from Spain or the Indies," he said. "It is not Christmas without those and without Malaga raisins, almonds from Arabia, and little bottles of scent from Spain. This is dangerous weather at sea."

The dusk of Christmas Eve had settled down as Amy lingered in Salem's Christmas shop. "I wonder where George is?" she said at last. "He was to have met me here long ago."

"There was a rumor this morning," the shopkeeper told her, "that a ship had been sighted. She was having trouble with the heavy sea. The town boys are all out watching for her. There is a prize of money, you know, Amy, for the Salem boy who first sights a ship riding in from a voyage to the Orient."

They went out and stood in the snow, which had begun to drift softly down on the evergreens that curtained the wooden shelter of the shop. Down Essex Street they spied a twinkling light, approaching, growing brighter until they saw a brass lantern throwing its beam of light along the snow. A boy in a warm blue ulster and knitted cap and muffler carried the lantern, running, and shouting as he came.

"First sight of a ship! The *Juno* is in from India with a cargo for Christmas! First sight of the *Juno!* Christmas ship!"

"It's George Lee!" Amy shouted, running to meet him.

The keeper of the Christmas shop smiled wisely as he laid out the pile of wreaths to be delivered at Amy's house. "A seaman's son, George Lee," he said, chuckling. "He will have a ship of his own one of these days, and he'll never let a meeting with a lass keep him from his duty. Amy will always have to wait until his ship comes home to Salem."

At Christmas dinner at Amy's house, everyone admired the gifts the captain of the *Juno* had brought George and Amy. George, for his skill in carving the figurehead that had taken the *Juno* safely on her first voyage, was given a set of carved ivory chessmen. Amy's gift was a gold wishing ring. It was so skillfully made that it opened out into four sections to make a perfect little globe. She was to keep it always, and her grandchildren and great-grandchildren, too, treasured it.

As Amy's father carved the Christmas turkey and heaped the blue Canton plates, he said, "A fine ship, the *Juno!* It has been remarked down at the wharf that her figurehead would bear a striking likeness to our Amy here, were she dressed like an angel, with her hair let loose from those long braids."

There was silence at the table. It was George and Amy's secret, and that of Captain Enos Briggs. George spoke at last.

"I'll be taking out my sailing papers in the New Year," he said, "perhaps for the *Juno.*"

"I am going too," said Amy firmly. And everyone laughed, for then the secret of the figurehead was out.

Sister to the little sailing ship, the ocean liner made by machines, manned by hundreds instead of a score of seamen, takes today the same route as did the *Juno.* But the ocean liner follows in the wake of the vessels made in the shipyards of old Salem. They left her their charts. Captain Enos Briggs, George Lee's father, and the rest of the seafaring men who built the clippers and guided them to China and the Indies, started our vast ocean commerce of today. Their logs, the garden of the figureheads in Salem, and the ghosts that walk Essex Street and the old wharves tell us this story and many others.

BETSY'S NEW HAT

TROT-TROT-TROT! "I'm happy, happy, happy!" Betsy Metcalf's happy heart kept time to the beat of her horse's hoofs as she rode, side-saddle, in to town with the week's supply of butter and eggs from her father's farm for the Providence market. She was an odd little figure. Twelve years old in the year 1799, a country lass who lived the other side of Smith's Hill from Providence, was Betsy. Her stiffly starched blue-calico dress and white apron billowed over the saddle, and her big sunbonnet did its homely best to hide the bright curls that made a frame for her rosy cheeks and starry eyes. Market day was a red-letter day for Betsy. In her pannier-baskets carefully balanced on either side of the saddle, white

eggs, round yellow cheeses, and pats of golden butter
wrapped in large grape leaves were packed in dew-wet moss.
As she left the hill farms behind and passed the white courthouse on the crest of Smith's Hill, Betsy stopped a moment.
It was a fair scene that lay below in the town of Providence.

Beyond the river that ran up close into the land and
lapped The Parade and Town Wharf sparkled the blue
waters of Narragansett Bay. Along The Parade and the
length of the curved waterfront called Walker's Point were
many shops whose gayly painted wooden signs flapped in the
wind. The shipyards were there, too, and there stood Jacob
Whitman's smithy, where ironwork for ships was welded.
Whitman, the smith, exchanged horseshoes and ironware
with the shoemakers of near-by Lynn, so one could buy
shoes for boys and girls as well as have a horse shod in the
smithy.

"Shoos, Gloshes, Clogs," said his sign, and as Betsy urged
on her horse and clattered down into the town, she looked
at her own well-worn shoes. But it was not a pair of two-
shilling shoes for which she longed, but something much
more exciting.

It was harvest time and the winding road that followed
the river was sweet with the last of the summer's roses and
clover. Betsy's horse wanted to crop the thick grass, but she
hurried him on. The sound of a distant drum came to her
and as she left the river road and came trotting along the
cobbled main street of Providence, she had to rein her horse
sharply to give the road to the town crier. He marched
along, drumming, and calling in a clear voice, "Organ music
Saturday night in Kings Church! Come one, come all!"

As she rode on, Betsy imagined that her horse's hoofs kept time to music. A great organ with two hundred pipes had been brought from England in 1772 to Kings Church in Providence. Betsy's mother had told her how wicked the deacons had thought this idea of having organ music in church. Even in Betsy's time, all entertainments and plays were forbidden in the town, but the organ at last sent its ringing chorals through the church. The drummer's words gave Betsy an added joy in the day's marketing. A girl of twelve would feel ashamed to wear a calico sunbonnet to Kings Church for the organ music. She was going to buy herself a new bonnet.

"Make speed, Dobbin!" she said, and they came at last to the public market where bargaining housewives and shrewd farmers, cackling geese, and wagons loaded with fruit and vegetables showed that this was the Providence market day.

Betsy dismounted, tied her horse to a post, and went in and out of the crowd with her baskets. "Fresh butter. Large eggs. Rich cheese," she called. Jostled, pushed about, her young voice almost lost in the loud cries of the farmers, she at last sold her wares. She carefully put the shillings she had been paid in the pocket of her dress, gave Dobbin the oats that she had brought from home in a saddlebag, and ate her lunch, an apple turnover and a piece of cheese, in the shade of a tree. Then she started out upon her shopping adventure. She had a free hour and she would use it well.

She walked back toward the courthouse and looked in the window of a bookshop whose sign showed the portraits of King George and Queen Charlotte of England. Almanacs, spelling books, and books of hymns were for sale; also, the

proprietors, Ephraim and Jabez Nightingale, were selling
something new, labeled "Powder for Preserving the Teeth."
But Betsy went on. She turned back to the little street of
shops that lay near the river and was called Cheapside. She
found a shop that sold bright English prints for dresses,
lawn from India as thin and soft as a summer cloud, "taffa-
ties," "Persians" of red and blue, "duffils" in black and blue
and other fabrics of silk and wool that our fast merchant
ships were bringing from far-off ports.

Betsy went inside and touched the pretty stuffs longingly.
She knew that she could not have a new dress that season.
She shook her head at the clerk, and went out. All the shops
on Cheapside were delightful. "The Sign of the Frying Pan
and Fish," where one could buy note paper, iron pots, and
copper kettles. At "The Sign of the Boy and the Book,"
bright pewter mugs and platters, inkpots from England, and

red calico could be had. Then there was "The Sign of the Elephant," where Master James Green sold tea, flax, indigo for dying homespun, and brass bowls. "The Sign of the Golden Eagle" offered scarlet broadcloth for cloaks for ladies and gentlemen when traveling, buttons, grindstones, looking-glasses, and lace. At "The Sign of the Boot" large firkins of butter were set out. Betsy skipped from one sign to another until she came to the shop called "The Sign of the Hat." Here she went in.

Stone crocks for holding the winter's jams and pickles, canisters of pepper and spices, sacks of flour, cakes of chocolate, and strong-smelling Cheshire cheese surrounded the bonnets, but Betsy went straight to that part of the shop where her dream lay. On a table, quite alone, was a beautiful imported Dunstable straw bonnet, wide-brimmed like a hat, and trimmed with ribbon and flowers. It was made, the label said, of Bermuda plait, which was a new kind of braided straw, never before used for bonnets. Betsy clasped her hands as she stood in admiration. She fancied herself walking grandly into Kings Church in that straw bonnet, for the organ music. She had never had a bonnet so beautiful, only cotton sunbonnets in the summer and a quilted woolen hood for winter.

The shopkeeper came out of a corner, lifted the bonnet and twirled it about.

"Good Master Balch, how much is it?" Betsy asked.

Nathan Balch, the proprietor of "The Sign of the Hat," sighed. "One pound," he said. "And I shall never be able to sell it this season at that price. It came by ship to Providence,

the only straw bonnet in the town, but too costly. I must pack it into its bandbox until another spring."

One whole pound! And Betsy's mother had said that she might spend one shilling of the market money for herself, but even that shilling was needed at home. Betsy pulled her sunbonnet down over her eyes to hide her tears as she went slowly out of the shop. She found Dobbin, untied him, and rode slowly home with her empty panniers.

The day was glowing with the sunset as Betsy climbed the hill, rode down the other side, and along the farm road home. As she put Dobbin in his stall, the reapers came into the barn with great bundles of oats upon their shoulders. Some of the straw dropped to the barn floor and Betsy gathered it up. It was golden yellow, soft, and pliable. Why, she suddenly saw that this common field straw was as pretty as the straw from which the beautiful Providence bonnet was made! Betsy sat down in the late sunshine of the barn door. She carefully split the straw with her fingers and plaited it into a braid. As in the story of Rumplestiltskin, the straw grew into gold. Before supper time Betsy had plaited quite a bundle of straw braid, and after supper she began carefully sewing it into the shape of a bonnet, with a wide brim that would tie under her chin. She sang as she stitched. Making the best of things had always been Betsy's way, but she did not know, sitting there in the candlelight making her own hat, that she was binding a new page of our history.

Saturday night Dobbin made another trip to Providence with Betsy and her mother on his back, riding in to Providence for the organ music at Kings Church. A very smart

and beautiful Betsy now! She wore her best pink-calico dress with white ruffles at the neck and sleeves. A homespun cloak covered it from the dust of the road. As she dismounted and went into church, not even the great ladies who had arrived by coach from Boston could boast of so stylish a bonnet.

Betsy wore, after the manner of the times, a close-fitting lawn cap with narrow ruffles. Over this was the home-made straw bonnet, its wide brim tied under the little girl's chin with cherry-colored ribbons dyed in the home dyepot. About the low crown lay a rosy wreath of everlasting flowers, gathered from a home lane and also dyed by Betsy. She felt very happy as she went in and sat down.

Betsy Metcalf's straw bonnet was the talk of that long-ago evening in old Providence. She was surprised the next day to receive a letter from Master Nathaniel Balch, begging for directions for making hat-plaiting from straw. During all that winter Betsy and the other Providence girls, the church sewing circles, the dame schools, and the housewives were busy making the straw braid that was sewed into bonnets for the coming spring. The harvest fields were full of gleaners gathering straw, which was split into seven strands and plaited. Bobbins were used for quicker braiding, and the girls and women carried their bundles of straw about with them. The art of making straw bonnets became as much the style as knitting.

Betsy Metcalf became famous. Old records tell us that orders for her straw bonnets came from forty miles around Providence. And as she grew from a girl to a young lady, and then to a woman, she was known as the one who made the first straw hat in our land. No other millinery was so popular

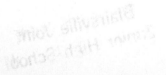

in New England as hers. With the making of straw hats came all kinds of other delightful millinery styles: making flowers and feathers, using lace and silk for trimming—there were even straw bonnets and hats made for dolls. The sailing ships were beginning to bring us fashion plates showing the stylish ladies of the French court, and Betsy copied these. Sunbonnets and hoods were quickly forgotten.

Ears that had been hidden, adorned with coral earrings, now peeped out from beneath the wide brims of hats. Dyes made from moss, from sumac leaves, from indigo, from cochineal, colored the hats green, tan, blue, and pink. The weaving of silk ribbon became a new industry in our land, for bows of rainbow colors and wide strings for tying beneath chins were needed. Little apples, plums, and grapes were made from scraps of silk and, with green silk leaves, were made into garlands for bonnet trimming. After a while boys and men took up the fashion of the straw hat, and hat factories opened all over New England.

The story of twelve-year-old Betsy Metcalf of Providence comes to us from neighbors who knew about the first straw hat she made because she could not afford the one at "The Sign of the Hat." She kept up her work all her life. When she was eighty, she was still making hats. We might not have had our hat factories, our bright millinery shops, our new hats for Easter, if a disappointed little girl in a sunbonnet, so many years ago, had not made up her mind to make the best of things.

WHEN JOSHUA MADE A BOOK

IN THE candlelight of the log cabin young Joshua Gillett of old Buffalo was looking at the composition book he had made. He sat beside the fireplace, for it was a bitterly cold December night, turning the pages of rough brown paper filled with his father's fine handwriting.

"Sylvanus Mabee—Eight dollars and a keg of nails.

"Joshua Gillett—Fifteen dollars, boards, shingles, and hand labor."

So the list continued through the pages, telling how the townsmen of the little frontier town of Buffalo Creek, near the great waters of Lake Erie, had helped to build a school-house for the children.

"Be careful, son," his father said. "That is the only record we have of that meeting at Joseph Landon's Inn, when we planned the school."

"Yes, I will be careful," young Joshua said, but he was thinking, as he slipped the book into a crack in the log wall that served for a secret drawer, that his father would not have had a blank book for the school records if his son had not made it. Joshua had saved squares of rough brown wrapping paper from the store. Then he had cut them to make pages measuring six and a half by four and a half inches and stitched them neatly between board covers. Joshua had planned that he and his friend Eliza Cotton would fill the pages with spelling lists and fine writing, for even when there had been no school, the children worked at their lessons at home.

But just as Joshua had finished stitching the book, his father had needed it. Little could be bought in the small trading post of Buffalo except corn, furs, and a few tools. James Robbins kept the blacksmith shop where horses were shod, and Indians often came to have their tools and tomahawks sharpened. Ezekial Lane kept the cooper's shop where barrels were made and heavy iron tires fitted for the wagons that were the settlers' only means of conveyance. But nothing could be bought for the children. A stout, hand-made composition book was a treasure, but Joshua had willingly given it up.

Outside, the dark night had settled down with no sound except the crackling of frozen twigs and the cries of an owl. One could not be sure, Joshua knew, whether it was an owl or an Indian's call, but the savages along Lake Erie, led by Red Jacket, Second Sachem of the Senecas, were friendly to the settlers. Young Joshua had a few pieces of wampum that Red Jacket himself had given him. The log house where the Gilletts lived was one of the best in Buffalo. From the ceiling hung strings of peppers, ears of corn, and drying apples. The chairs were slabs of logs set on legs pegged in at the corners. The beds were built into the walls: just poles, long and short, inserted into holes in the logs, and laced with bed cord. There were bear skins and Indian blankets to snuggle in.

But there was nothing for a boy to do in the evening. Joshua decided to go to bed. Lying there, warmly tucked in, he watched the fire burn lower and the long shadows made by his mother's spinning wheel where she sat beside it in a corner. Half-asleep, half-awake, he remembered Christmas in the schoolhouse his father had helped to build. Tonight was the thirtieth of December in the year 1813, and the school party had been held the week before. Their little log schoolhouse was almost five years old. All the town had helped to build it, making a party of raising the walls, laying a wood floor, and putting in the lights of glass that made the windows. The children sat on long hard benches, made of split logs set up on pegged legs. There were not enough schoolbooks to go around. There were no black-boards, pictures, or desks. But through the doorway, open in the summer, Joshua and his friend Eliza could see into the green spaces of the forest. Often a flash of color or a rustle of soft moccasins on the pine needles told them that there were Indians about, but the children were used to them. Through the trees they could sometimes see the blue water of Lake Erie.

The big lake had been the reason for the settling of the frontier town of Buffalo a few years before. Across its blue waters came the Indians, their canoes piled with the precious furs which were taken across the waterways of New York State and down to New York where they were sold. Following the wilderness trails westward, Joshua's family and Eliza's family, riding in covered wagons, bringing their cattle and sheep and their cooking utensils and tools, had come from New England to find their fortunes. But so far there had been little save hardship. Trouble had arisen this year. Joshua had heard about it in the store, the blacksmith shop, and in the dooryard of the Inn. A British ship had anchored in Lake Erie, near the head of Buffalo Creek. The British, coming down from the North through the St. Lawrence River, were as eager as the settlers of Buffalo for the fur trade, and were said to be arousing the Indians against the settlers. The settlers planned to retaliate. But there was nothing for a boy to worry about, Joshua thought, as he pulled the coverings up close to his nose and listened to the wind blowing a gale outside.

The last bright coals of the fire made him think of the candles on the Christmas tree they had trimmed in school. It was a hemlock from the near-by forest, so tall that it reached the roof. Strings of popcorn, gingerbread figures made by the mothers, bright knitted clothes for dolls, neckties, mittens, mufflers, and carved wooden toys had covered the Christmas tree with joy. Carol-singing, speaking of pieces, games, molasses taffy and apples had finished the school party. It still seemed to this boy of the forest one of his best good times.

The fire was burning low and as Joshua, just ready to drop off to sleep, looked toward the tiny window in the side of the log wall across from his bed, it seemed reflected outside on the snow. This, though, was impossible. But the street was red. Moving torches flickered along, in and out of the woods, like will-o'-the-wisps. Then the torches came along the main street, where their flames streamed above the heads of the Indians who carried them like scarlet banners. Joshua sat up in bed. His father went to the door and returned white-faced.

"It's Indians and soldiers," he said. "Our troops tried to take that British ship and now the British are burning the town. The Indians are lighting the houses down Main Street and the wind is coming this way. We'll have to take to the woods."

While Joshua was getting into his buckskin breeches and coat, his father harnessed their wagon and brought it around to the door. The town was one great flame by that time, so quickly had the fire spread. Soldiers in blue and in red, swarthy Indians giving savage war cries, shrieking women and children, smoke and the crackling of flames terrified Joshua. They wrapped his mother in blankets and helped her into the wagon. While his father held the half-crazed horses, Joshua got together a few things from the house, his jackknife, the spinning wheel, the brass andirons, and the copper teapot. He found Eliza Cotton and her mother, and room was made for them in the Gillett wagon. The horses started, and the Gillett wagon joined the trail of sledges, wagons, men, women, and young folks on foot, fleeing through the deep snow of the forest from the fire.

All night the flight continued. Some had to drop out. Others from near-by fur posts joined the procession as it struggled along. It was cruelly cold. Joshua wrapped his jacket about Eliza's shivering shoulders, for she had only a shawl. When they passed the flaming schoolhouse, the Christmas tree sent out a sweet scent into the night as it burned.

"The wooden doll you carved for me burned with our house, Joshua," Eliza said, trying not to cry. "There was no time for me to bring it." Joshua showed her the jackknife he had saved. "I will make you a better and bigger wooden doll when we find a new home," he told her.

When the fleeing people, cold, frightened, discouraged, reached the lighthouse on the bluff, they were told that nothing was left of their town except the ruins of two of the larger log houses. Morning came, as cold as the day before, and the heavy snowfall covered up even the forest trails. The fathers and mothers were sad indeed but the children, tough little backwoodsmen, looked upon the fire as an adventure. The Gilletts were fortunate in having a wagon. They helped others, giving them lifts in turn. They spent one night in an Indian hut. Joshua and Eliza sat side by side on bear skins before the fire that burned under the kettle in the middle of the hut. It lighted the faces of the kind red men who shared their venison stew and corn mush with the wayfarers. Joshua was given a fine bow and arrows, and Eliza a pair of warm moccasins. They started on again in the morning, rested, warm, and well fed.

There was nothing to do but ride on, with occasional stops at the camps of woodsmen or fur trappers. New town sites were looked for, but none seemed as good as the old one.

As the weather grew milder, as ice and snow melted, the Gilletts and their neighbors turned back along the shores of Lake Erie and began building Buffalo again.

For some time they could not afford a school, but logs were cut for new houses, James Robbins opened another blacksmith shop and Ezekial Lane his cooper's shop. Fields were plowed and corn planted. Fruit trees were set out, and spinning wheels began to whir again. The fire that had destroyed Buffalo did not kill courage, and fireplaces soon glowed above the ashes of the conflagration. Joshua's family set up their housekeeping again, and so did Eliza Cotton and her mother, the children helping as much as they could. New chairs and tables were hewn, and beds built along log walls. Peddlers driving through from the East brought pots, pans, and bright cloth to make new dresses and aprons and shirts. Spring came, and the Buffalo fire was forgotten.

But there had been one tragedy. All the important papers that held the town's records had been burned. Records of the deeds to property, marriage and birth records, the books and diaries of the settlers had all been burned. These had been valuable, especially the deeds to land, the boundaries, the records of sales, and those of taxes. If there had not been a spirit of neighborliness among the settlers, the new Buffalo might never have been built, but people remembered exactly where certain houses had been, where their old fields and gardens had been laid out. They did not quarrel about boundaries.

The Gillett family moved into their new house, and put into place the few things they had carried about for weeks in their wagon. A small tin trunk had come all the way from

New England with them, and young Joshua had hastily filled it on the night of the fire. They opened it and took out, to everybody's surprise, not only the silver spoons and candlesticks, but the hand-made composition book.

"Look, Father," Joshua said in excitement, "the book I made has come back with us! It tells all about when our school was planned."

His father took the book in his hands as if it had been bound in gold and lettered in illuminated script. "Why, lad," he said, "you saved the only record, our school record, left from the fire."

That was just what had happened. Joshua had taken the book from its hiding place in the wall and put it in the tin trunk. He had loaded the trunk into their wagon at a risk to his own life in the fire and then had forgotten it. But here it was, safe.

The hand-made book, telling how much those settlers of early Buffalo wanted a school for their boys and girls, how they built it with their own hands, is preserved for us in Buffalo today. In that city, the gateway to our Great Lakes and the vast shipping business of Canada and our West, Joshua Gillett's composition book is one of the city's most precious documents. The rough brown-paper pages are still firmly fastened with hand stitches between the coarse board covers. The signatures of the fathers who gave what little money they could, building materials, or the work of their hands, are still faintly readable.

If the children of that time in our history wanted a composition book they had to make it, and it was used only for their best writing and spelling, and had to last a long time. Today's composition books are made from cover tc cover by machine. Buffalo now has more than a hundred schools, in which trades and many other kinds of special training are given boys and girls free. Stone and bricks and steel, instead of hand-hewn logs, made these schoolhouses with their kindergartens, auditoriums, gymnasiums, cooking rooms, art studios, manual-training shops, and libraries. When these modern schools open in September, two hundred thousand composition books, perhaps more, will have been bought by the school department and given to the school children. So it is in other cities of our land. How splendid if these blank books might make history as did Joshua Gillett's old hand-made one so many years ago!

COVERED-WAGON BOY

SWINGING HIS legs from the lazy-seat, playing a jig on his new harmonica, Daniel Moyer rode home from Philadelphia to Linglestown in his father's covered wagon. The lazy-seat, a sliding board of strong white oak pulled out over the left-hand side from the driver's seat, was difficult to balance on. But a stranger was riding home with Daniel and his father, and he sat beside Herr Moyer under the big top, so there was no room for Daniel. The boy was enjoying the thrill of sitting over the wheel. He was not interested in the scraps of talk that came to him above the jingle of the bells the horses wore on their yoke. It had been a great trip and his thoughts were keeping time to the tune he was playing.

Never before had he gone with his father on a trading trip in their great covered wagon. They had started out two days before. Herr Moyer had carried a load of firkins of rich golden butter, hand-dipped candles, fowls for the market, and some precious peppermint oil, home-distilled, for a Philadelphia druggist. Daniel had also carried a store for trading: some hog bristles to sell to the brushmaker in town, bags of walnuts, and a brace of rabbits. On the way they had been joined by other covered wagons bringing loads of farm produce and flour to Philadelphia. Young Daniel had got his new harmonica in trade.

On the way to Philadelphia they had hurried the big horses, stopping for brief meals at inns along the road where the innkeeper gave them for a few pence mugs of steaming coffee, bread, honey, and apples. The public market in Philadelphia near Independence Hall was a busy place, thronged with traders from miles back through the Conestoga Valley. It was colorful, the bright paint of the wagons splashing out against the gray of Quaker coats and the homespun of the wagoners. The Moyer wagon was among the brightest. The six-foot wheels and sideboards were painted vermilion, and the running gear a clear blue. Daniel was proud of their wagon, made from tires to shafts under the direction of their Linglestown wagoner, Herr Zentmeyer.

Now, rolling home, they drove more slowly. They had spent last night in the open, the wagon serving for a tent and the hobbled horses crunching the rich grass. The horses wore their bells all night to warn other drivers, but their sound was like an echo in Daniel's ears, mingling with the tinkle of the sheepbells and cowbells farther away. His father had opened the wallet he had filled in Philadelphia with food for the return trip, jerked bear's meat, rye loaves, and cheese. Daniel had hardly finished his supper before he had gone to sleep, rolled up in one of the blankets inside the wagon. He had not bothered to try to find out from their talk who their guest was.

Nor had the boy listened very carefully when they started along in the morning. He found his new harmonica a real delight, a bit stiff, but his wind was good. By noon the roadside began to look familiar because they were nearing Linglestown. Grist and fulling mills, great fields of cabbages being raised for sauerkraut, apple orchards smelling like his mother's rich apple butter, log houses with high-pointed gables, and huge barns with stone ends, overhanging eaves, and double doors came into view. The big, patient horses, bred in the leafy Conestoga Valley for wagon use, stepped out faster as they neared home. Steam rose from their sleek round bodies. A bend of the road and they were home at last. Daniel made a flying descent from the lazy-seat. His mother, wiping floury hands on a calico apron, met them at the gate. Herr Moyer introduced the stranger with some ceremony.

"This is Monsieur Latour," he explained, "whom I have brought from Philadelphia to teach our Daniel to play the piano. He will come to us regularly and teach our Daniel to be a fine musician, a pleasure to us in our old age."

His father's words confirmed Daniel's worst fears. A few weeks before, a spinet, the tiny piano of our early days, had come in their wagon for Daniel. He knew now that he was to be made into a home boy; perhaps, some day, the organist of the Linglestown church, and he had made quite different plans for his future. It was the year 1810, and Daniel Moyer was thirteen years old. It was at the height of the pioneering excitement in Pennsylvania. Like a long colored pageant

Daniel saw the Conestoga wagons pass along the road in front of their farm, their bells chiming, trailing, winding into the sunset along a blue-grass road, disappearing into the foothills, on their way through the Cumberland Valley to Ohio, and farther. The boy wanted to go with them.

These wagons, with their families, tools, household goods, seeds, and building materials, were opening our West. They took their name from a tribe of peaceful Indians, the Conestogas, People-of-the-Forked-Roof-Poles, who had found shelter in William Penn's woods and still lived in palisaded villages along the banks of Conestoga Creek; Daniel and the other boys had visited these Indians. He and his chums had followed the wagons as far as their feet could take them. It was Daniel's life dream to take his place on a wagon seat, snap his whip, and ride through the forest, over the mountains, into the West.

It seemed to him that he could not endure sitting through supper beside the music teacher, Monsieur Latour. He slipped out of the house, some bread and cheese in his pocket, and hid behind the woodpile. Although it was very uncomfortable, he stayed there until the stars came out and he fell into a troubled sleep. No one thought of looking for him there. Daniel woke at cock-crow and, without thinking how worried his mother must be, he set out. He had no real plan except that of following the wagon trail.

As Daniel trudged along he passed wagonloads of lumber on their way to the shops where wagons were made—great lengths of swamp oak, white oak, hickory, locust, gum, and poplar that would be shaped into squared planks, boards, and spokes. He passed the town smithy where the blacksmith, an

honored man in Linglestown, was forging wagon tires at his small brick hearth forge, hammering the strip of iron at his small anvil, then fitting it around a great wheel. A wagon stood or fell as its wheels were made, Daniel had heard his father say. These wheels were as tall as a man, and the wagon body was shaped like a ship. Daniel had never seen the sea, but the covered wagon in which he planned to embark some day would be his bark of discovery.

On he went until he came to the shop of Herr Zentmeyer, the wagon-maker, at the edge of the village.

"Where away, young Daniel?" the wagon-maker called, and the boy, tired and hungry, stopped.

"I have left my home," he told Herr Zentmeyer. "They would make me into a piano player and I want to drive over into Ohio."

Herr Zentmeyer thought for a moment, shaking his head. Then he went to the back of the shop and brought out an ornamented tool-chest. It was a rare piece of work, decorated with ironwork in a design of trees of the Black Forest in Germany, Zentmeyer's homeland. Inside was a fine collection of hand-made tools, a hammer, wrench, hatchet, and pincers. The tool-chest had curved iron supports by means of which it could be hung, together with a tar bucket and a water pail, under a rear axle. No covered wagon could start out without a tool-chest.

He put the chest into Daniel's hands. "I will give you this some day if you will return home now, obey your parents, and learn to build a wagon before you drive one," he promised. "You are but a lad, young Daniel, and the trail needs men, not boys. All my life I have wanted to go beyond the mountains, but there is no one hereabouts who can put together such stout Conestogas as I. I have learned that my work is here, and you, too, young Daniel, must learn that lesson." He put the tool-chest back again on a shelf.

Daniel sniffed the perfume of fresh wood and paint that filled the shop. He looked at the tall skeleton of a partly completed wagon out in the yard. He remembered the bows with which Herr Zentmeyer was greeted when he changed his cap for a beaver hat and went to church.

"You are probably right, Herr Zentmeyer," Daniel said at last. "I will go home."

"Run then," urged the wagon-maker. "It will go better with you if your father has not started to fetch you."

Fortunately, Monsieur Latour was waiting for him, and Daniel's mother welcomed him without too many questions. By the time his father came in from the fields, the music lesson was going so well that he did not interrupt it to punish Daniel. At supper that night, Daniel spoke of Herr Zentmeyer's promise of the tool-chest.

"Of course I intended that you should learn a trade," his father said. "Next year if you have done well in school and learned to make music for your mother and me, I will see if Herr Zentmeyer will take you as an apprentice. The country needs strong wagons more than anything else. It is a good trade for a boy to learn."

So, in another year, Daniel Moyer started to learn the wagon trade. He lived at home and went on with his practicing, for his father loved music. But his working hours became as full of adventure as those he had planned to spend driving out West. Under the teaching of Herr Zentmeyer,

Daniel learned first of all how to make a strong straight wheel spoke of white oak, first by working it down with a hand adze, and then placing it in a vise and further shaping it with a draw knife. From making spokes, he progressed to the shaping of the broad hickory hoops that sometimes stood as high as eleven feet from the ground and held up the homespun hempen top. Daniel had to climb a tall bench to reach them.

Then he learned how to shape the great boat-like frame that made the body of the wagon. He became skilled in metalwork, beginning with the welding of the flat brass hoops from which the horses' bells hung in a row. He learned how to shape the iron band that encircled the hub of the wheel. At last he was old and strong enough to help at the anvil with the welding of the tires. He soon earned Herr Zentmeyer's tool-box. It swung beside Daniel's own wagon when, still hardly more than a boy, he became a wagoner.

Those were stirring days in our country. The westward trail of the covered wagons was drenched with blood. Not all the Indians were as peaceful as the Conestoga tribe. The road from Philadelphia to Pittsburgh, the gateway to Ohio, was filled with wagons carrying pioneers, building materials, and food. Many of the wagons returned bringing furs, skins, and wheat. Daniel took his place among the drivers of the latter.

He wore a wide-brimmed hat, a homespun suit, and high top boots, for sometimes he had to ford a stream, wagon and all. When bleak winter came, he put on a fur-lined greatcoat and home-knitted mittens and wound a wool scarf about his neck. He carried a rolled mattress upon which he slept under the big wagon top. His bells made a shrill jingling as he drove along. The many other wagoners whom he had helped out of tight places with Indians or weather had given him, as was the custom, their hame bells; these bells his horses wore in addition to their own.

Daniel Moyer still longed for adventure, however. He was doing what we should now call trucking. He had not been farther away from home than the foothills of the Cumberland Mountains. He would have loved to ride farther and never come back, but his father and mother needed him. He was playing the piano in singing school, and he was the bugler of the Dauphin County cavalry; neither of which positions seemed to him of great importance.

"Only a wagoner," Daniel was thinking one day as he returned home with a load of flour. "I don't see any chance of ever having an adventure." Then, as he wheeled the great wagon around the turn of the home road, he saw that something out of the ordinary was going on. Flags were flying from the little stone houses. The cavalry was gathering in front of the Linglestown church. Cheers greeted him.

"Get your bugle, Daniel Moyer," they called to him. "We are called to Harrisburg for a review."

Daniel did not wait to hear any more. He unharnessed and fed his horses. He put on his uniform, tried out his bugle, and joined the cavalry. He was the loudest, clearest bugler anywhere about. As they clattered along the Harrisburg highway, troops and townsfolk met and joined them. The little town was in gala dress. Daniel took his stand at the head of a welcoming company. Suddenly the Marquis de Lafayette approached, stopped, and saluted the bugler whose silver notes made the gallant Frenchman think of the courage of this country that he loved so much.

As he sounded taps on the evening his cavalry troop rode home, Daniel felt that adventure had truly come to him at last. Suppose he had been out on the plains when he was needed at home? Well, he had not been. He had found out that adventure often waits at one's doorstep, and hard work brings reward.

This covered-wagon boy lived and worked many years ago. Over the ruts of his wheel tracks, concrete now spreads a smoother road. Long freight trains, motor trucks, airplanes have crowded the covered wagons into museums, where they stand, with tattered canvas and arrow-scarred framework, to tell us of those other days when human hands were building our greatness. Daniel Moyer, the boy of old Pennsylvania, was never more than a wagoner, but General Lafayette saluted him, and his townspeople remembered him and left us his story.

The Flag House

STAR-SPANGLED BANNER GIRL

CAROLINE PICKERSGILL had learned to sew as soon as she could hold a needle. While her mother kept their little red brick house in old Baltimore spotless and shining, while she polished the brass candlesticks, scoured the floors, and spread the linen out on the garden grass to bleach, Caroline sat beside her grandmother Rebecca and stitched—first the long seams of hand-woven sheeting, so long and stiff for little fingers to hold; then a calico dress for her wooden doll. That was fun! After that, she embroidered scallops for pantalets and petticoats, and matched the countless tiny squares of colored cloth that made the pattern of patchwork quilts. Caroline could hardly have been patient enough to sit sewing,

115

quiet and industrious, in her small red rocking chair, if old Rebecca, her grandmother, had not told her stories to shorten the work. They were thrilling stories, for Rebecca Young had made a flag for General Washington to carry when the American army took part in the siege of Boston.

The story always began with Rebecca's description of her Philadelphia flag shop. She had even advertised her craft in the *Philadelphia Ledger* in the days of the Revolution:

Colours
For the Army and Navy, made and sold at the most reasonable terms,

REBECCA YOUNG

In Walnut Street, near Third Street, and next door but one to Mr. Samuel McLane's.

N.B. Any person having Bunting for sale may hear of a purchaser by applying as above.

That was how her advertisement had been printed. Then Caroline's grandmother Rebecca would go on to tell of the visit of General Washington to her shop, of his order for a flag which should have thirteen stripes of red and white, one for each of the Colonies. In the corner of this flag was a "grand union" of the old British flag, a blue field with the red and white crosses of St. Andrew and St. George.

Soon after this flag was delivered to General Washington, Rebecca had been obliged to flee with her children in an ox-cart going West. Her silver spoons and the Bible had been lost in the forest. There had been her struggle in the wilderness of western Pennsylvania, and then their return to this pleas-

ant home in Baltimore. The entire countryside remembered how Rebecca had made General Washington's battle flag. Beautiful needlework was their family pride, Rebecca told Caroline. Her own fingers were too stiff now to take the tiny stitches for which the family was celebrated, but Caroline's mother, Mary Pickersgill, who had been only a baby when they fled from Philadelphia, still made flags occasionally. Perhaps some day Caroline also would stitch well enough to sew together stripes of red and white bunting, her grand-mother said.

Peace and happiness filled the house where these three, Rebecca, Mary, and Caroline, lived alone. Caroline's father was dead, but they owned their brick house near the water-front in Baltimore, and Mary made a fair living for them stitching more and more of the banners that Caroline watched going out toward the sea, flying above merchant ships and sailing vessels. The American Revolution was nothing but history to the little girl, hard to believe when the bees hummed drowsily in their garden and the hens clucked contentedly over their nests. But Caroline often wondered at what she saw from the Baltimore wharf.

She loved to go down to the wharf, just a step from their front gate, and follow with her eyes the crimson trail her mother's flags made as the ships bearing them put out to sea from Chesapeake Bay. For almost two years many of these flags had been pulled down before they were out of sight; seamen had been taken from the American ships by British cruisers, and sometimes the ships themselves impressed into British service as the property of England if captured on the high seas.

Still this War of 1812 meant very little to Caroline Pickersgill. Other matters seemed to her vastly more important. Bonnets were much fancier in Baltimore than ever before because the girls and ladies were copying the clothes of the French Court. Caroline was making wreaths and bunches of silk flowers, a bombazine frame, and a piped green silk covering for her doll's bonnet. From scraps of her mother's bunting she had made the doll a blue cloak with a red lining, the stylish French colors. It was now fully two years since her mother's banners had first been torn from ships' rigging, and the small town of Baltimore still dozed beneath its white church steeples, its elm trees and flowering hedges. Caroline had come to think that the British and American ships were playing a game out there at sea, and by means of it helping give her mother more work. For Mary Pickersgill made a new flag for every one torn down and tattered, and Grandmother Rebecca folded each one carefully, sending it to sea with her blessing.

It was August of the year 1814. Caroline had never been so happy before. She was a tall girl now, with a flowered bonnet of her own, and with daintier dimity and muslin dresses billowing about her silk slippers than almost any other girl in Baltimore had. She was fourteen years old, and she could sew better than any of her friends. She made all her own clothes, from her embroidered chemises to the lace mitts that reached from her slender wrists to the edge of her puffed sleeves.

Sewing was not Caroline's only hand skill either. Her mother spent all her time in their flag shop, too busy to do the housework. Rebecca was seventy-five years old, and growing blind. She sat in the garden all summer long, trying to see the colors on the ships as they sailed out, and in the winter she huddled by the fireplace, telling over again the story of General Washington's visit. Caroline did the family sewing, baked bread, tended the garden, kept the pewter plates and the silver spoons shining, and raised the largest potatoes and the brightest hollyhocks in Baltimore. She also sold honey and eggs, and was always invited to quilting bees because she could quilt faster than most women. Her days were filled from morning till night with things to do and be happy about.

But all Baltimore was not as peaceful as the Pickersgill flag shop on Albermarle Street. What seemed at first to be the thunder of a summer storm was the roar of British and American ships' guns. After two years of sea warfare and the capture of American seamen by British captains, American ships had begun to imitate the methods of pirates. Many of the vessels sailing up and down the Atlantic coast were now privateers, a polite name for prize-runners. If British ships can impress our sailors, we will take their cargoes, these privateers said. A quarrel between nations that might have been peacefully settled two years before, had blazed into warfare, and at last Baltimore was threatened. British ships seeking a fleet of American privateers were on their way to attack and hold the tiny brick fort built in the shape of a star, which stood, surrounded by cow pastures and hay fields, on a low peninsula guarding the town. There seemed no hope for Baltimore. Danger such as the townspeople had not known since the Revolution stalked at their very doorsteps.

But it was adventure, not danger, that lifted the brass

knocker of Caroline Pickersgill's front door on that long-ago August day. She ran to open it, and curtsied as three townsmen entered in haste and excitement. They were the three officers in charge of the few troops that Baltimore had been able to muster. According to old records of this visit, these neighbors were Commodore Barney, General Stricker, and Lieutenant-Colonel MacDonald. Their swords hung at their sides, their anxious faces were gray in the candlelight, as they spoke to Caroline's mother.

"Fort McHenry will not stand a day's siege from British guns," they said. "Our good neighbor, Dr. Beans, has been taken a prisoner of war. Our only chance is to trick the enemy into thinking us stronger than we are. We desire, Mistress Pickersgill, that you make at once a great American flag. We want this banner to measure at least thirty-six feet long and twenty-nine feet wide. Four hundred yards of bunting will be delivered to you here in a few hours if you consent to help us. What say you? Can you deliver this flag to the fort before we are attacked from the sea? We hope that so large a flag will speak to the enemy of the high courage of our land."

"At once, good sirs," Mary Pickersgill answered. "As soon as the bunting arrives, I will begin cutting."

"Do your best, Mary," urged Rebecca, tapping the brick hearth with her cane. Then going back to her dream world, she said: "Do you not see General Washington and his aides there in our doorway, come to us for a battle flag?"

"Couldn't I help with the sewing?" begged Caroline, her eyes shining with excitement. "Surely, Mother, you can trust me to stitch stripes together." So the three, old Rebecca,

young Mary, younger Caroline, daughters of the Stars and Stripes, promised to do their part in protecting their town.

The mammoth rolls of bunting were delivered at their house promptly that night, but, alas, it was soon discovered that there was not a room large enough for cutting out the flag. The parts had to be cut to fit exactly, mostly upon the floor. Much of the sewing also was done on the floor, Mary Pickersgill kneeling down and stitching each stripe, each star. What should they do? At last, in the early morning, with the help of soldiers, they carried the bunting to a deserted malt house that stood near the fort. There, on the great floor, Mary cut, basted, and stitched. Caroline ran between the malt house and their home, taking stripes to be stitched, caring for old Rebecca, and returning to kneel beside her mother to add her fine seaming to the completion of the flag.

The flag had not been started a moment too soon. Disturbances in Baltimore had begun. A group of British soldiers had broken into the garden of Dr. Beans, a well-known townsman, while he was serving tea to some friends. The intrusion had resulted in the arrest of the doctor, who was imprisoned on one of the enemy ships as a British prisoner of war. Ladies in crinoline and silks had scattered, leaving their jasmine tea, sponge cakes, and ices untouched. A gentleman guest, young Francis Scott Key, a Baltimore attorney, had gone at once with a flag of truce to attempt the doctor's rescue. He was now aboard the American cartel ship, the *Minden,* in Chesapeake Bay two miles from the town. Should the attack upon Baltimore from the water be successful, it was rumored that the town would be set on fire.

But the flag was finished—red, white, and blue, six times as long as a man is tall, secure against storms because of the firm hand-stitching of Caroline and her mother, and bright with the courage of patriotism. They watched it being carried to Fort McHenry and raised upon a tall pole behind the guns.

In the early morning after the flag-raising, the attack upon Baltimore from the water began. For twenty-four hours British mortar ships poured bombs, rockets, and red-hot shot against the little fort, tearing gaping holes in the earth, and piercing the brick walls. A few rents were made in the flag, but it waved bravely in the sunshine. Never had such a flag taken part in battle. Aloof and peaceful, it floated above the fire of the attack. After a day of terrible shellfire and a night of the same horror, the fort still stood. The great banner stitched by Mary and Caroline Pickersgill billowed

in the wind as the attacking fleet sailed away, defeated as much by the seamstress's art as by the brave militia of Baltimore.

From the water, Mr. Francis Scott Key watched the flag all that night, as it flew above the red of the rockets and the smoke of the bombs. He could not tell whether the British or the American forces were victorious. In the morning of its triumph, when he and Dr. Beans were safe on land again, he wrote a poem about the flag. We may surmise that Mr. Key wrote this poem under the protection of the red-brick walls of Fort McHenry, with green grass for his carpet and the Stars and Stripes as a canopy:

> Oh, say can you see by the dawn's early light,
> What so proudly we hailed at the twilight's last gleaming?

There were many stanzas to the poem, but each ended:

> The Star-Spangled Banner, oh, long may it wave,
> O'er the land of the free and the home of the brave.

Soon, everybody in our country was singing Mr. Key's song about the flag that Caroline had helped to stitch. We still sing "The Star-Spangled Banner," and the old flag itself is kept as one of our most precious relics of American history in the Smithsonian Institution at Washington. The Pickersgills' house on Albermarle Street in Baltimore is well remembered; the ancient sewing baskets, the old candlesticks, the stiff straight chairs, the steel shears for cutting bunting, the sewing table, just as they were when young Caroline learned how to make a flag.

Today huge machines cut, stitch, and bind our flags. Our dresses, suits, even dolls' clothes, are fashioned by machines, and the days of patchwork quilts and hand-made banners are as far away as is Caroline in her flowered bonnet, long muslin frock, and small silk slippers. But the boy or girl who visits the Smithsonian Institution in Washington will marvel at the tiny stitches Caroline set in the Star-Spangled Banner.

THE BOY WHO MADE PENCILS

FROM THE window of the pencil factory in Concord, Massachusetts, Henry, standing beside his workbench, could see and hear the river. It was the year 1837, and Henry Thoreau, a country boy of old New England, was home from college helping his father. What he truly longed to do was to build a boat in which he and his brother John would voyage all the way along the Concord and Merrimac Rivers, miles away from their home village, until they reached the White Mountains. Not even Harvard College had changed Henry from the little boy who could always learn more from the Concord meadows and Walden Pond than from a book. He did not like to make lead pencils, but this did not keep him from doing his share in the factory.

Concord in those long-ago days was a small green-and-white village, with the countryside and woods within a two-minute walk. Farmers, workmen, and tradespeople lived in its small white houses. It had a stage-coach route. Carters on their way to the mountains of New Hampshire passed through the village. When Henry, John, and Cynthia were children, their father had kept the general store in Concord. In those days Henry used to start off with a piece of his mother's good pie and an apple in a basket, to wander about all day in any direction. With his big jackknife he whittled the wood he found into a whistle, a gun, a slingshot, or a toy wagon. Sometimes he made a trap for rabbits. He played Indian by himself, ate a meal of huckleberries, dug a cave on the banks of the pond, built a hut there, and stored it with nuts, berries, and firewood.

The outdoor world was Henry Thoreau's picture book, and he could not bear to be imprisoned between four walls. He and John swam for hours in the Concord River, with its pine trees spreading their branches above them like a magic green roof. Haytime, cranberry-picking time, the sight of a slow-moving barge floating along the river toward some unknown town, the day when their meadow was filled overnight with wigwams and strange red men in blankets and feathers, these were the great moments of this boy's life. He had gone to school only because his father wished it.

In order to pay Henry's school bills, his father had decided to open a pencil factory in Concord. It was right that the boys should help him, but making a pencil in those days was a long, tedious job. A great deal of the work was done by hand, and the finished pencils were crude and much more expensive than those we use so freely day in and day out.

Henry was slowly spreading glue upon the grooved pieces of cedar wood into which the graphite mixture was to be spread before the two parts of the pencil were put together. The cedar wood, fine and aromatic, from New England forests had first been cut into thin slats. These slats had been carefully dried to prevent warping. When Henry's glue was dry, the long sticks that held the leads would have to be cut into the right length for the finished pencil. A drop of glue too much or too little, and the pencil would be spoiled. The pencils must be sandpapered with the utmost care. Paint must be mixed and put on.

If there had been any carelessness in blending the powdered graphite, bayberry wax, and glue that made the filling for the pencil, it would be spoiled. Henry knew the reason for this only too well. We were at that time not able to make as smooth a graphite in this country as they did in Germany, whence the best pencils came. The boy idly sketched on a piece of board the boat he planned to make. No, the Thoreau pencils were not as good as the imported ones. The lead broke easily. They did not make a broad smooth stroke. They could not be sharpened to draw a fine line. They cost twenty-five cents each, a large sum for that time or even for today.

It would have been an easy matter for a boy who disliked his daily work to give up and run away. Henry Thoreau knew that he could easily take care of himself in the woods and on the water. He had the outdoors skill and understanding of an Indian. He was happier under the sun and the stars than in this factory. He felt as if he knew the great cedar and pine trees, the squirrels, the birds, the tides, and the

winds better than he would ever know people. He threw
down the glue brush and looked at his cap hanging on a nail
beside the factory door. This making of pencils in Concord
was a hopeless job. He had just returned from a trip with his
father to New York to sell pencils. They had not had a pay-
ing trip, for the German-made pencils were widely used.
There was a man named Faber in Germany who had discovered a secret formula for mixing graphite, and no pencil mixture in our country could come anywhere near it for
smoothness and strength. Why not give up the business and
just live like a happy animal, Henry thought. But he picked
up his glue brush again. He kept on working until there were
so few orders that his father said he might take a vacation.

John and Henry Thoreau had planned for years to go all
the way by water from their little village of Concord to the
White Mountains. They set to work now to make a boat. In
a week their boat was finished. It was a heavy strong dory
with a sharp bow such as fishermen like. It was fifteen feet
long and had a coat of green paint with a blue border. To be
ready for any emergency on their trip the boys gave their
boat two masts, two pairs of oars, and wheels so that it could
be rolled on land around waterfalls. They put in a tent and
a buffalo skin for a blanket, a few tools, cups, tin plates, and
a frying pan. Their main cargo was a pile of melons from the
home garden and a sack of potatoes. They rolled the boat
down the bank and into the waters of the Concord River.
Then they were off!

The two boys pulled straight ahead, not tiring for miles.
On the banks the haying was being done. At night they could
draw into a shallow cove, cook their supper on the shore, and

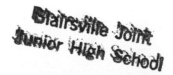

sleep under the shelter of a haymow. Sometimes they spent the night in the deep woods, when the hooting of an owl might be the warning call of savages. A farmer's wife sheltered them during a bad storm. They hoisted their sail and weathered another storm. The sluggish, slow-moving waters of the Concord River changed to the dangerous rapids of the Merrimac, and still the two Thoreau boys were safe and having the best time of their lives. They passed Amoskeag Falls, as steep as a staircase. The boat overturned and they had to swim, pulling it along part of the way. They reached the White Mountains and, leaving their boat at a village wharf, climbed the 6,288 feet of Mount Washington.

Then home again, back to Concord, where they landed, tired but happy, just two weeks from the day they had started, and tied the boat to an old apple tree. It had been a brave adventure.

As he tied a sailor's knot in the boat's rope, Henry thought about his splendid trip. He had never cared very much about writing compositions in school, but he could make a great story of their boat trip on the Concord and Merrimac Rivers. He searched his pockets, but he had forgotten to bring a pencil. He scuffed the soft earth of the river bank with his hobnailed shoes. Nothing but work in the factory tomorrow! How splendid it had been to drift along the river, to sleep in the boat, to light a fire on the bank and cook the fish they caught, to pass like a bird to unknown shores! As he stands, digging his toes in the clay of the river bank, let us look at this boy of old Concord.

He was small, as lean as a wolf from walking and running outdoors, his shoulders bent from working at a bench, and there was an expression on his face of a wise and experienced gnome. His clear eyes were gray but tinged with the color of blue skies. He had light brown hair and he was sunburned until he was almost the hue of an Indian. His hands were those of a working boy, and he wore rough homespun clothes, the jacket faded green. But when he looked at you, you knew at once that you would like to take a walk with Henry Thoreau. There was a friendly twinkle in his eye. His whole body breathed the open air.

He was just deciding that he ought to walk home when he looked down at the earth. The clay was soft and smooth where he had been digging into it. Could this be the secret of the smoothness of the German Faber's pencils, that the leads were made soft, black, and strong by being mixed with clay? The boy fairly dashed back to the factory with a handful of clay in his hand to talk his idea over with his father. It was more than an idea. It was a discovery. The Thoreau boys did not make any more trips that season, for the pencil factory began to thrive.

The neighbors wondered at the secret work going on in a little building that was put up close to the Thoreaus' house. No one was allowed to share the secret, but these pencil-makers of Concord had been able to obtain a shipment of fine, rich clay from Bavaria. They discarded the bayberry wax and glue in mixing the graphite paste, and instead were making pencil leads of finely powdered clay and pulverized graphite that, once hardened, would glide over a piece of paper with a beautiful gray-black mark. Very shortly Henry Thoreau's pencils had taken a first prize at the exposition of mechanical arts in Salem. With the entire family working in the mystery of their primitive workshop, carving, mixing, gluing, polishing, painting, the Thoreaus were soon making the best lead pencils in America, and shipping them all over the land at six dollars a gross.

Being a fine craftsman did not change the boy Henry. He still spent all his spare time outdoors, walking miles, from one season to another, in any kind of weather; scrambling to the top of a pine tree to scan the horizon for an Indian campfire; finding the first mayflower of the spring and the last empty bird's nest of the fall; making a roof of bark with his knife the instant a storm overtook him; plunging like a savage into a thicket of brush and tough vines in the woods, instead of going around it; wading the mud of a swamp to find out how frogs live; tasting apples in a wild orchard after the frost had made them sweet; fighting a snowstorm; whittling his initials in the bark of an oak tree: H.H.H., Henry, Happy Heathen. Was not that a good way to live?

Ever since he had been old enough to walk, Henry Thoreau had loved Walden Pond. It was close to Concord, but so secret among its deep and overhanging forests that a boy could feel himself in another land on its shore. In the hills back of it, it was said, had lived escaped slaves, witches, old pirates, and Indians. In the winter a boy could walk to Walden Pond, skate out to the middle, cut a hole in the ice, and lying flat on his stomach watch the fishes flitting about in their icy home. In the summer it was good to strip off blue calico shirt and homespun suit and plunge into the water for a swim. Henry decided to build himself a cabin on the shore of Walden Pond. Here, when he was not needed at home, he could come, and with one of the new pencils write a few pages of the book that had come into his mind.

The people of Concord, shut safely within their gardens by white gates, thought this boy, Henry Thoreau, crazy. What, they asked, was the need for chopping down trees, sawing boards, building a cabin on the shores of Walden Pond, miles away from a human being? But Henry built his cabin, gathered stones to make his fireplace, fitted together logs to make a bed, a table, two chairs. He built a cupboard in which he kept the bowl for his morning porridge and for his supper of berries and milk. Whenever he could leave his work in town, Henry lived the life of a happy hermit here.

He bathed in the pond, watched the changing flowers and leaves of the changing seasons. He cooked his simple meals, with sometimes a rasher of bacon for a treat. He even learned to like a meal of bitter boiled chestnuts eaten from a bowl as he sat at his doorway, the squirrels chattering and the blue water at his feet. The second year, his garden at Walden Pond yielded corn, peas, beans, and turnips. This second year, also, there was other fruit of his labors. The hermit was finishing a book.

When Henry Thoreau held in his hand the first copy of his book *A Week on the Concord and Merrimac Rivers,* he noticed at once the odor of the glue from the binding. It reminded him of the days, many years before, when he had been gluing together the best pencils he could, and then had discovered how to make better ones. He thought of his vacation, how he had returned to his father's workshop, and how, together, the pencils and his boat had made this book. When *The Journals* about early spring in Massachusetts, summer, autumn, and winter, were printed, telling of what the boy

Henry Thoreau had seen on his walks about Concord, the cabin on Walden Pond found its way, too, between book covers.

The books that Henry Thoreau wrote were to be read for many years. He had been able, with the pencils he made, to record on the pages the song of the wood thrush at evening, the splash of oars as two boys paddled into the sunrise, the taste of huckleberries, and the chill of the swimming pool. Every library and many homes today cherish Henry Thoreau's books, for few American naturalists knew the outdoors as well as he. They have been translated into many foreign languages. The little village of Concord became famous because Henry Thoreau lived there. But the story of his pencils is not so well known, and it belongs with those of our other workers who did something to be proud of with their hands.

The working plans of a skyscraper or a giant bridge, the pictures for a book of adventure, the drawings in our art museums, the score of a symphony or an opera, the story that millions read—all these begin with pencil strokes, and remind us of a boy who made pencils by hand when the river called him to run away.

LOST IN THE APPLE CAVE

SWINGING HER worn shoes from the steps of the covered
wagon whose great canvas top had been her only roof for
months, Rose looked back along the wilderness road. At its
beginning lay the mountains. Where the road ended was a
wide river. Rose and her father and mother were on their
way from New England to that great unknown place beyond the Ohio River called the West. Everything they owned
was packed in the great clumsy wagon, camped now on the
banks of the Ohio until a flatboat should come to ferry it
across. Rose had loved everything about the trip: the slow
movement along strange roads, the tinkle of bells on some
peddler's mule, the glimpse of a passing wain full of barrels

of maple syrup or of raw hides and raw wool, the evening's camp beside some brook with a supper of cornmeal mush and salt pork cooked over an open fire.

The big wagon was like home to the twelve-year-old girl. In a corner crowded with pewter plates, patchwork quilts, sacks of cornmeal, and gourds of milk, Rose had a family of dolls made of great pine cones she had gathered on the road. She had dressed them in bits of her own calico frock as it had become torn. The little heads of these dolls, made of small wild apples, wore sunbonnets like Rose's own, or hats made of plaited rushes gathered by the brooks. The pine-cone dolls had a set of dishes made of acorns.

Kicking her heels against the wagon step, feeling the warm harvest sun on her bare legs, Rose wished that she knew what lay within those deep woods at the right of their camp. She was sometimes lonely, for they had not happened to meet any other girl of her age all summer. She watched her mother bending over the knitting she was trying to finish before the sun dipped down into the river in flaming crimson. Her father was trying to catch some fish for supper. Rose stood up at last, swinging a little hand-made basket over her arm.

"I am going for a walk, Mother," she said. "Perhaps I can find some berries in the wood to eat with our porridge to-night."

"Do not go too far, Rose," her mother warned. "Your father saw a big brown bear quite close this morning."

"I will be back by suppertime," Rose said.

In five minutes from the time she left the wagon camp, Rose was out of all sight and sound of it. The faint stir of a passing snake among the fallen leaves in the forest, the rustle of a chipmunk's little feet, the flapping of a crow's wings or an owl's, were the only sounds. Rose hurried, remembering the bear. She never thought that she could lose the trail, but soon it seemed as if she were going round and round, each moment straying deeper into the wilderness. Her arms and legs were scratched by the bushes, each step was less sure. Rose ran. She clung to the little rush basket for comfort. It broke the force of her fall as she stepped down, tumbled, and found herself imprisoned in a cave. The entrance had been carefully screened by leafy boughs and bushes. When she got up and looked about, Rose could not believe her eyes.

The cave smelled deliciously of apples. Eating apples were a new fruit in those days, and rather rare. But here, in a roomy cave that had a little bubbling spring at the back to keep the fruit moist, was shelf upon shelf of wonderful apples such as Rose had never seen, stored away for the winter. There were August apples, the delight of harvesters. There were great golden pippins which made Rose think of the big bell on the church at home that had rung for their courage when the covered wagons started out; hard little russet apples that would keep all winter and be sweeter in March than they were now; and great red spicy apples, grown by grafting a shoot from a wild-apple bough into a bough of a sweet orchard-apple tree. Rose selected one of these apples and sat down in content on the mossy floor to munch it. This might be a bear's cave, she thought, but it was the pleasantest place she had seen in a long time.

Bright skin, delicious juice, crunchy pulp, Rose ate her apple down to its nest of big black seeds. She was just cupping her hands to drink from the spring, when a shadow darkened the door of the cave. Could it be the bear of whom her mother had warned her? Rose was dumb with terror as she saw a dark form closing the cave entrance. But a voice reassured her.

"Don't be afraid, little girl. It's only Appleseed Johnny. Welcome to my orchard!"

The man, strange indeed with his long hair, ragged clothes, and feet bare save for Indian moccasins, held out his hand to Rose.

"Come and see my trees, little girl," he said. "Many of the people of the covered wagons make this orchard of mine their halfway house before they cross the Ohio River. Come and see my house, too, and then I will show you the way to the camp again."

As the man led Rose out of the cave and into a clearing where grew more apple, cherry, peach, and plum trees than she had ever seen before, he talked about himself. He was still a young man, but he said that he had traveled on foot to Pittsburgh all the long way—across mountains, fording streams, and breaking trails through the wilderness—from Springfield in Massachusetts. His name was John Chapman. He was called Appleseed Johnny because he was the only orchardman of the pioneers. He loved apples, and he knew how much the West needed fruit. The rich soil was fairly aching to nourish the seeds that he had begged from farmers in Pennsylvania and planted there on the banks of the Ohio River.

Appleseed Johnny showed Rose the shed where he sorted and washed apple seeds, started shoots for new trees, and kept his spade and pruning shears. Then they went into the big comfortable cabin he had built for himself of forest wood, lusty logs of oak, chestnut, and pine. An apple bough, gnarled and crooked into the shape of a forest gnome, was perched on the ridge of Appleseed Johnny's cabin for its roof-tree. The nails that held the cedar planks of the door were hand-made. So was the star-shaped iron latch that Appleseed Johnny lifted as he opened the heavy door and led Rose inside.

In the light of the big stone fireplace the girl thought that Appleseed Johnny looked like an Indian, as brown, sharp-eyed, and slender. He gave a low call, and down from a shelf near the roof fluttered a fluffy sleepy little owl and nestled on his shoulder.

"I came too far away from our wagon," Rose explained. "Folks say there are bears in these woods."

Appleseed Johnny laughed. He went to the door and made an odd growling sound. Fascinated, Rose saw a shaggy brown animal lumber out of the gathering darkness, sniff at Apple-seed Johnny, and then pass by.

"All the wild creatures love this appleman," Rose thought.

Appleseed Johnny came in and filled a big pewter mug with milk for Rose. He put a comb of golden honey and three red apples in her basket. Last, he gave her a little apple tree, no taller than her pine-cone doll, and a small deerskin bag of seeds.

"Now I will guide you to the edge of the woods," he said. "And when you come to your new home in the wilderness, set out this young apple tree in the sunshine, and water it and build a little fence of brush about it to keep off the deer.

"In this bag are precious seeds of other apples, of berries, pears, cherries, grapes, plums, and peaches. Plant them and

tend them, for there is no fruit in the wilderness. Your mother will want berries and fruits for her autumn pies, and jellies and preserves for the winter. Your new home in the West will need grapevines growing over it, and a pink cloud of orchard blossoms in the spring."

As Appleseed Johnny talked, he led Rose safely through the darkening forest until she could see her own campfire and smell the fish her mother was cooking.

"Good-by, and thank you," she said.

"Good-by, Little Pioneer," he said. "Remember Appleseed Johnny and plant your trees."

"I will!" she called as she ran over to hide her little tree and the seeds. She ate supper in a dream and in her sleep smelled apples under the canvas top. A flatboat was waiting for them in the morning, and they drifted, wagon and all, over the Ohio River and into the wild lands beyond.

Season after season Appleseed Johnny tended his trees, harvested his fruit, and sorted his seeds. He kept cows and had a row of beehives. Season after season the covered wagons carrying hundreds of pioneers West stopped by his cabin. The travelers were fed apples, honey, and milk and given little bags of Appleseed Johnny's precious seeds.

Rose's covered wagon rolled on into the untilled, wild country of Ohio. Her father told her about Appleseed Johnny. "He was only a boy when he left his home in Massachusetts and tramped out to Pennsylvania," he said. "He took apple seeds in payment for work for the farmers, and he built his house and planted his orchards with his own hands. Hundreds of covered wagons stop at his door, rest, and go on, carrying his bags of seeds."

On, on went the wagon until Rose's father found a farm site. The seasons passed quickly, with so much work to be done. The land was cleared and a cabin built in two years. That was the year that Rose picked berries from the bushes that grew from Appleseed Johnny's seeds. In four years roads were built, the cabin made larger, and Rose's dresses were longer. That was the year that she picked peaches, cherries, and plums from the trees planted from Appleseed Johnny's seeds. In six years Rose was a young lady. It was another October, and the apples from the little tree that Appleseed Johnny had given her were harvested and waiting in the kitchen to be made into apple butter for the winter. Rose would trust no one but herself to do this.

In the sunny kitchen she had set out empty pans, tubs, sharp knives, and a great basket of juicy red apples. On linen thread, hanging from the beams of the kitchen were strips of apples drying. The strong crane in the open fireplace held a brass kettle filled with pared apples, sweet and sour in proportion, the sweet ones at the bottom, with quinces and molasses added for flavor. She had put straw in the bottom of the kettle to keep the cooking apples from burning. Rose would spend days preserving the apples for the winter. Down cellar, tubs of apple sauce would freeze and keep through the winter as sweet as when it was made. The dried apples would be made into pies.

Rose stirred the apple butter, her back to the open door. Suddenly she heard a low call, like that of a little screech owl. She turned and saw a surprising figure.

The man was as tall and straight as an Indian, keen-eyed, and on his back he carried a great sack. He was as ragged as a beggar, his hair had grown to his shoulders and he wore Indian moccasins. He gave his bird call again, and smiled at Rose. "You have grown, my child," he said.

"Appleseed Johnny!" she cried.

"Yes, I am Appleseed Johnny, still planting orchards in the wilderness. I gave away my house, filled this sack with seeds, crossed the Ohio River in a dugout canoe, and have been wandering for many years, scattering seeds, and teaching the pioneers how to plant and tend orchards."

"Come in," Rose begged. "Spend the night with us, and let us feed you as you fed me when I was a covered-wagon girl. These are your apples that I am cooking. Your little tree lived, and every one of your seeds grew and gave us fruit."

An old letter tells us the rest of the story: how Appleseed Johnny, pioneer nurseryman of the early nineteenth century, spent the night in the Rice cabin, made welcome by Roselle Rice and her family who had passed his door many years before. Many covered-wagon children knew Appleseed Johnny, but Rose was the only one who wrote about him. In the morning he started on again. He carried a Bible in the sack with his seeds, and left one leaf of it with Rose. Then he tramped off into the woods farther West and she never saw him again.

But Appleseed Johnny walked for forty years, leaving his little buckskin bags of seeds and his Bible pages at lonely cabins, planting the orchards that now cover acres of the West, sleeping outdoors, making friends with bears, wolves, and foxes, looked upon by the Indians as the Great Spirit. Pioneers went on with his work. Today skilled orchardmen cultivate the vast tracts of fruitland of our West. Following the trail he started, great freight trains return now to the East carrying barrels of Jonathan, Winesap, Spitzenburgh, Northern Spy, Delicious, King, Greening, and Golden Pippin apples for hungry boys and girls. The wild hardy stock poured into the spiced sap of the cultivated growth still gives us new, larger, tastier apples. The sturdy covered-wagon people, going West, gave us our beautiful Western cities, our fertile farms, our fine schools. And every pink apple blossom of the spring is scented with Appleseed Johnny's kindness to little Rose, and every bite of a rosy October apple tastes as sweet as those he laid away in his cave.

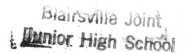

A BASKET FOR THANKSGIVING

THE FARMER twins, Susan and Eliphalet, hung over the stair railing and peered down upon the gay scene of the husking bee. It was the week before Thanksgiving in old Boscawen, New Hampshire. Susan and Eliphalet were children of our homespun days, and the harvest season, when the corn was stripped of husks and shelled, was one of the year's holidays. All the young people of the village were gathered in the Farmers' great kitchen, making merry as they piled baskets full of yellow kernels and heaped huge piles of corn husks.

It was like looking down upon a stage. The kitchen, now that the short November day was darkening into late afternoon, was bright with candles set in tin holders that Susan

146

had polished to silver brightness. The pitch-pine knots that Eliphalet had gathered in the woods beyond the Hollow flamed crimson. Two pumpkin jack-o'-lanterns carved by the twins sat grinning on the shelf over the fireplace, among pewter mugs and plates. On the sideboard there was spread the feast which Susan and her mother had made ready. The Dutch oven beside the fireplace had been full for days. Hasty pudding to be eaten with rich golden molasses. Earthen pots of hot baked beans. Fried apple turnovers. Doughnuts. Gingerbread and yellow cheese. Apple pies. Pumpkin pies. A pleasant hum of talk came up to the children, accompanied by the rasping sound of the ears of corn rubbed against the sharp handles of tin frying pans, brought by the guests to save their fingers in the corn husking.

In a corner of the kitchen near the fireplace, leaning against one of the corn shocks brought in for decoration, an odd figure of a man was curled up.

"Nathan sleeps," Susan said, pointing to the visitor who wore a faded Indian blanket, moccasins, and homespun breeches. "All he came for was to beg corn husks left from the husking to make his baskets."

"Those who do not work must expect to suffer," Eliphalet observed piously. "We have heard Deacon Little say that often enough in meeting."

Susan's forehead wrinkled in thought. "But Nathan Hunt does work," she said. "The baskets he weaves are honestly made and very useful. They do say there is no better basket-maker this side of Boston."

"He has done no husking," her brother insisted stubbornly, "while our fingers are sore from the sharp kernels. There he sleeps waiting to be roused for his supper. One, two, three, go!" And down from the stairs, plump on the old basket-maker's head, fell the overripe pumpkin that Eliphalet had saved for this prank. It burst. The basket-maker was covered with pulp, seeds, and confusion. In a burst of laughter, for husking time was an occasion for pranks, Nathan disappeared, leaving a trail of orange pumpkin on the freshly sanded kitchen floor, out into the twilight, and toward the Hollow.

"For shame! Who played this unkind joke?" Mistress Farmer asked. "Nathan Hunt brought me this morning one of the finest woven baskets for sifting grain that I ever saw."

But the twins slipped down into the crowded kitchen without being caught. Susan hastened to pass plates for the husking feast, and Eliphalet had a sudden errand out to the woodshed to bring in more logs for the fire. Just then the fiddlers who were to play for dances after supper arrived, and someone began singing. The old basket-maker was forgotten, and the fun that followed the day's husking began.

Not altogether forgotten, though. As Susan piled a platter with doughnuts, she touched her little brown sewing basket that stood on the dresser. Nathan Hunt had made the basket for her, that she might carry her pincushion, needles, and thimble in it to a quilting bee, or spend a happy evening at home sewing for her dolls in the candlelight. Willow splints and fragrant rushes from Mill Brook, sweetly scented with the pine needles that Nathan had woven in for decoration, made the little work basket. The feel of it touched Susan's warm heart. She beckoned to Eliphalet, who was trying to husk a few left-over ears of corn, unobserved, behind the settle.

"Which would you rather do, Eliphalet Farmer? Eat your supper on the road or take the birching that awaits you? Our mother's eyes are sharp and she knows who dropped that squashy pumpkin on Nathan Hunt. I have a mind to take Nathan's husking supper to him. There is time before the husking bee is over. And if we are both away on such an errand, you may avert the rod and I a tongue-lashing."

"I will go with you," the boy decided.

It took but a moment to put some food in their pockets, and wrap an apple turnover, some cheese, and doughnuts in a linen cloth. Eliphalet gathered up the bunch of corn husks that the basket-maker had dropped in his hasty departure. Susan put on her bonnet and cape, and Eliphalet his warm cap. His thick tow shirt, homespun cassimere clothes, and buckskin leggings were protection from almost any weather. Mistress Farmer, busily serving the huskers, did not see the twins as they slipped out of the kitchen. In a few moments they had left the Plain, where they lived, and had dipped down into a darkening north road that led into Boscawen's Hollow, the Valley of Industry.

In the daytime the Hollow rattled and clashed and banged. There the town sawmill and the flour mill hummed, their great wheels turned by the rushing flow of Mill Brook. From the Hollow, on the swift currents of the Merrimac River, hundreds of pine masts, spars, and bowsprits floated down to Lowell and Boston for the shipyards that launched vessels sailing to the Indies and China. There in the Hollow rang the coopers' hammers making staves and iron hoops for the barrels that traveled on flatboats to Boston, to hold molasses, sugar, and beef.

The Boscawen boys and girls loved the Hollow. There they could sail boats on the brook, gather blocks of wood for their building, and go nutting in the forest from which came the sweet-smelling logs of pine, white and red oak, poplar, hemlock, and chestnut that were shaped and turned into ships' spars at the sawmill. But the valley was now still. With the dropping of the sun behind Clay Hill, which lifted its wooded peak west of the Hollow, the mill wheels rested, forge fires burned out to ashes, and the Valley of Industry was given over to the wild creatures that hid in the forest by day.

"There is a price for a wolf pelt posted on the meeting-house door. Two shillings," Eliphalet said as they trudged along through the dusk. "I would have been wise to bring along a musket."

"Oh!" Susan gasped. "Why speak of wolves? Hark!"

The dry grass and bushes behind them rustled with padded footsteps. Susan gripped her brother's arm. He looked back, straight into two great gleaming eyes.

"A wolf is following us. Run!" he said. The two sped on, losing the path in the darkness, finding it again, panting, always pursued by the stealthy four-footed steps. They ran pell-mell into a man in front of the sawmill who was as surprised as they. The lantern that burned in the mill window all night showed that they had overtaken Thomas Courser, the village herb man, on his way home to his cottage in the forest. Thomas's basket of thyme, summer savory, mint, and sage flavored tasty stuffing for roasted ducks and turkeys. The children of Boscawen were dosed with his home-made medicines and blistered with his mustard plasters. Everyone knew him.

"Thomas, good Thomas, save us!" Susan gasped. "We are pursued by wolves."

Thomas peered into the dark road. Then he chuckled. "Puss! Puss!" he called, and a great black cat came purring out of the darkness and rubbed against his legs. Behind came another cat and another. Thomas Courser threw them some sprigs of catnip from his basket. "They are the flour-mill tabbies," he said. "They must be about their mousing all day, but when I start home they will follow me a mile for a sprig of catnip. Where are you bound for at suppertime?"

Eliphalet was too ashamed to reply, thinking how he had run away from a mill puss. Susan explained.

"Well, good night and good luck," said Thomas, the herb man, as they reached the turnpike where he must leave them. "Nathan Hunt well deserves the feast you are bringing him." Soon he was only a fading shadow, a passing fragrance of mint and catnip carried by the night wind. The twins went on, Susan with her basket of food, Eliphalet with his corn husks, their free hands tightly clasped.

Once more they were startled by animals' footsteps in a field. They turned out to be only Deacon Little's flock of French merino sheep, crunching their supper of late grass. A little farther along the turnpike road they jumped, and their hearts beat faster as a menacing skeleton of a creature raised its arms to stop them. But they had just passed the shop of Tristram Noyes, who made farm tools by hand for Boscawen and the neighboring villages. What had frightened the twins was only one of Tristram's half-finished plows at the edge of the road.

A golden harvest moon rose at last to show them their way.

They laughed and waved at the jolly man in the moon. An echo joined them for company until they came to the end of the road. There under the shadow of Clay Hill, the twins saw candlelight spreading a narrow path to guide them. They ran on and came to the cottage shop of Nathan Hunt, the Boscawen basket-maker. Eliphalet rapped at the door, and when it opened, Susan held out her package of goodies. "We beg your pardon for dropping an overripe pumpkin on your head, Nathan," she said.

"It was I who did it, not Susan," Eliphalet said honestly. "And it was Susan as well who packed this supper for you and was minded that we come and beg your pardon."

The basket-maker chuckled. Then he laughed until the forest gave back his ringing laughter. He had removed all traces of pumpkin from his person, and his frugal meal of hominy and milk was on his table. It was said in Boscawen that Nathan Hunt grew plump on laughter. He was a poor man, but his cheery chuckles, as he went from house to house peddling his baskets, were as welcome as his wares. He laid out two more wooden plates as Susan opened the food they had brought.

"That pumpkin was a husking joke," he said. "I understood that you would not play such a trick on an old man except the occasion gave you the liberty. Draw up and share these good things. I know that Mistress Farmer's turnovers and doughnuts are not to be equaled in the village."

As the three ate in the candlelight, the children looked around the little cottage, crowded to the corners with Nathan Hunt's rushes, hickory and ash splints, willow reeds, and the golden corn husks that Eliphalet had brought. Sunny days the old basket-maker spent in the woods or along the brook, searching for the young trees which he would chop into basket lengths to be shaved down into splints. Rainy or winter days he polished his splints, made the hoops that fitted together and shaped the basket rim, the bottom, and the handle, and then wove the basket with skilled fingers that had learned their art from the Indians.

There was daily need for Nathan Hunt's baskets: for gathering apples, sifting grain, straining yellow curd before it was put in the cheese press, for holding the balls of bright yarn that Mistress Farmer and the other mothers of the village knitted into mittens and mufflers and stockings, for filling with nuts in the autumn. They were long-lived baskets that Nathan Hunt made, and he gave them beautiful patterns of corn-husk braiding, designs worked in pine needles, and slender willow borders like lace.

"You do forgive us, Nathan?" Susan asked, between bites of a doughnut.

The old basket-maker laughed again. They had finished supper, and Nathan brought out a big hickory basket as round as a melon, and woven so well that it seemed of one piece.

"I like a prank myself," he said. "But this you must do in penance. Here is a stout basket that will last a lifetime and longer. Use it for a Thanksgiving basket, to hold the fruits of the harvest, and to carry food to those who need it. Then I shall never think again that you tried to turn me into a scarecrow. I will lend you my lantern to light you home. Be off now, for the evening is on us and your mother will worry. Good-by and a good Thanksgiving Day!"

As Susan and Eliphalet started home, they could see for a long distance the light of the basket-maker's candle. When it was gone, the lantern made a bright path that guided them. When they came to their house, the huskers were still making merry, playing games and singing to the fiddlers' music. Their mother tried to look stern, but when the twins explained where they had been, all she did was give them each a plump square of pumpkin pie.

"You did well to ask Nathan Hunt's pardon for your mischief," she said. "We could hardly keep house or farm without his baskets."

That was a long time ago; for Nathan Hunt lived and worked in the little New Hampshire village of Boscawen about the year 1840. His name has come down to us as that of a basket-maker whose work was so carefully and beautifully done that it made history. Harvesting, preparing the grain for the miller, cheese-making, sewing, knitting, all our patiently wrought handcrafts were woven into the polished forest-scented splints of Nathan Hunt's baskets. The children loved his basketry cradles for dolls, his school lunch baskets with stout covers, his little sewing baskets that held patchwork squares, his baskets for young fishermen.

Machines today have taken away the work of the basket-maker, but we find his handicraft treasured in museums, beside that of the Indians. And each Thanksgiving Day we may remember him as we fill a basket for someone who needs it.

QUILT OF MANY STARS

REBECCA LEFFERTS had been shut indoors for three weeks. Snowdrifts had piled against the door of her log-house home; they had covered the barn, so that Tobias, her father, had been obliged to dig a snow tunnel through which he crawled to feed the cow and horses. The smoke-house, in which shoulders of pork were hung to cure over a fire of hickory logs and corncobs, looked like a little dwarf castle hung with icicles. The great pole that crossed and closed the toll-gate near their home, where Ohio spread over into Indiana, looked, in its cloak of snow, like a ghost. It was so cold that the Leffertses had hung their star-and-crescent bed quilt up inside the door for warmth.

Although the Leffertses had lived there in the Ohio Reserve for some time, they had not changed their Dutch ways. In a corner of the kitchen the Dutch clock, Old Long-String, that the first Lefferts family had brought from Holland, still ticked loudly. Its face was a map of the heavens, with twelve signs of the Zodiac beside the numerals. Blue delftware and pewter shone on the great Dutch sideboard that had come with the family in the covered wagon from Pennsylvania. The star-and-crescent bed quilt, which Rebecca's mother had helped her patch, had also come at that time.

It was a Pennsylvania patchwork pattern, the stars and half moons of different-colored calico pieced together with invisible hand stitches. The whole was quilted with about two thousand yards of hand sewing. It was set on homespun, filled with cotton, and backed with homespun. The Leffertses were proud of their young Rebecca's quilting skill. It was beautiful work for a girl of twelve.

But Rebecca, looking at the star-and-crescent quilt hung at their log door, saw in each tiny colored patch a small window of her heart. She loved the wide-rolling fields of the Ohio country, the little wandering creeks along which she walked in the summertime, with long-legged sandhill cranes for company. She loved Ohio apples and peaches, and the deep forest whose oak trees marched right up to her father's cleared acres. But she had never been to the schoolhouse, where, at hickory desks, the girls sat on one side, and the boys on the other. The Leffertses, even in Ohio, were still Pennsylvania Dutch in their thinking, and Tobias judged quilt-making more suitable for his daughter than learning to read and write.

But Rebecca wanted to go to school. She wanted to know other boys and girls. There, in the quilt, Rebecca saw a star cut from her brown-and-red calico dress. She had worn that dress to the church supper, but she had sat in a corner and come home early, for the other girls had not spoken to her. "One of those Pennsylvania Dutch people who are taking up land out on the Reserve," she had heard one of them say.

In the center of the quilt was a great design of crescents and stars made of turkey-red and white calico. Rebecca had been starting another crescent, sitting out in the orchard to sew, when a crowd of merry boys and girls had dashed by with picnic baskets. They had hardly seen her. Perhaps, Rebecca thought, they were unfriendly because she lived so far from the village, out there near the toll-gate. But she was a lonely little pioneer girl that February of the year 1841. After all, she sighed, three weeks of being shut in by snow-drifts was not much worse than being Pennsylvania Dutch in Ohio.

As Rebecca looked at her patchwork quilt, hanging like a bright tapestry against the logs, she could almost hear the creaking wagons that had passed their door until the heavy snows came. From Connecticut to Virginia and Kentucky, on to Illinois and Kansas, over the Santa Fe and Oregon trails, the great canvas-covered wagons had rolled by, carrying pioneers westward, and with them their patchwork quilts. When the wagons stopped in Rebecca's fields for a night, the quilts were brought out. They covered the babies. They hung for curtains at the back of the wagons. Sometimes on a cold night they were wrapped around the shoulders of the women, patched cloaks as bright as Joseph's coat of many colors.

Rebecca had learned to tell where the pioneers came from by the patterns of the patched quilts they brought with them. The beautiful Star-of-Bethlehem quilt, its great center star made of as many as eight hundred little calico diamonds, came from New England. From New England, too, came quilts with patterns of garden wreaths and baskets, straight furrows, pine trees, shells, and little red schoolhouses. Kentucky and the Boone trail, sending its wagons into Ohio, sent patched quilts in patterns of pineapples, peacocks, and spice-pinks. In her own state of Ohio, Rebecca had heard of a new quilt pattern of round red love-apples, those rosy fruits newly cultivated that changed their names at last to tomatoes.

But Mother Lefferts, plump, Dutch, and old-fashioned, saw no beauty in any quilt pattern except the star-and-crescent. One or two lonely tears squeezed themselves out of Rebecca's eyes and fell to the rag rug on the cabin floor. Only two tears, though, for Rebecca, red-cheeked, with two long yellow braids hanging down her blue homespun dress, was a young copy of her mother, as brave, and usually as cheerful. And just then, through cracks in the door, she noticed that the sun had come out. Her warm breath helped her to melt the frost on the cabin window and look out. The snow was melting.

There were no teams yet, but Rebecca saw a dark spot in the road from the village. It moved, grew, came nearer, and at last showed itself to be a boy's round head in a red knitted cap with earlaps. Then a green wool muffler showed, like a branch of green beside the snowy banks. A sheepskin coat, wool breeches, and feed bags tied over his boots came next. The boy came down the road and turned in the Leffertses'

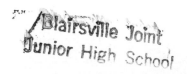

gate. He came along the path and rapped at the door!

"I'm Mrs. Scott's boy, Frank," he said as Rebecca let him in, and Mother Lefferts brushed him off with their buckeye straw broom. "There is going to be a quilting bee at our house today, and I thought you would like to come. I've seen you here when I go down to the grist mill. I have broken a path so you can come right along back with me."

"Oh, Mother!" Rebecca's blue eyes shone. Mother Lefferts was a little hesitant.

"Ach, yes," she said. "Your mother is a kind woman, but our pumpkins have all frozen and I have only squash pies baked. I should think shame to come to a quilting bee with so little."

Frank had seen the longing in Rebecca's eyes. Looking at each other they smiled.

"Oh, bring along the squash pies," he said. "My mother has roasted two big turkeys, and somebody is sure to bring pumpkin pies."

"I could bring six, then," said Mother Lefferts.

"I have no patchwork to bring," Rebecca said, remembering another difficulty. "I don't go to the school, so I couldn't fill a piece bag with different patches like the other girls." Her eyes dropped.

"That's a grand quilt," said Frank, pointing to the Dutch star-and-crescent on the door, so brightly red and white. "Bring that."

"I don't know the other children," Rebecca said. "We live so far out here, by the toll-gate."

"You know me now," Frank assured her.

So they started. The six squash pies filled a basket. Frank took Rebecca on one side and the basket on the other. Plump Mother Lefferts trudged on behind, with the folded quilt hung over her arm. They wore warm capes and quilted hoods. The sun turned the white road and fields to crystal, and it was not long before they saw the outbuildings of the homestead where the Scotts lived: the toolhouse, under the eaves of which hung scythes, sickles, hoe, rake, axes, quail nets, fishing poles, and husking pegs; the milkhouse with pots of cream, milk pans, crocks of golden butter, and the cheese press. Then came the well with its grapevine rope now crusted with frost, and the comfortable frame home, a story and a half high, the wings housing a great kitchen, a dining room, and a workshop, in the corner of which was a loom.

The kitchen was already full, and the great quilting frames with a patched quilt stretched upon each were laid on the backs of chairs. A roaring fire crackled in the fireplace, and the room was humming with the quilting bee.

"Anntje, here, goes to our school, and she came from Pennsylvania, too," Frank told Rebecca. "And here are Emma Badger, Sophia Howells, and Ellen Clark."

Rebecca was timid at first, but the girls smiled at her as Frank led her around the room. They sat about on stools with their bags of bright scraps of cloth—orange, yellow, snuff-color, maroon, plum, purple, and lavender—carefully stitching the patches that would sometimes be joined together to make their own quilts. Twelve women bent over the frames that filled the center of the room, their shining needles flashing in and out, quilting the patchwork to its lining of homespun.

Frank's mother welcomed Mother Lefferts. "You must excuse us for not having been out to see you," she said. "The teacher, here, is coming to see Mr. Lefferts soon about your little girl going to school. We are glad you could come to the quilting bee."

"I must ask your pardon," said Mother Lefferts, raising the cover of her basket. "Only six squash pies."

"How good!" said Mrs. Scott. "I tried to make mince pies with bears' meat, pumpkin, vinegar, and honey, and a little pepper, but I am not sure how they will taste."

"And this is our quilt," Mother Lefferts said, unfolding the red and white star-and-crescent patchwork. Rebecca blushed. The other girls had been showing her some of their Western designs for patches, a bear's paw, the harvest sun,

sheaves of wheat, Cleveland lilies, and pioneer cabins. They would know by the pattern of her quilt that she was a Dutch girl.

But everyone at the quilting bee exclaimed as the star-and-crescent quilt was unrolled before them. It was truly wonderful, they all said. In the center was the great pattern of many small diamonds made into a star, with crescents between the points. Red crosses made the border. The red calico glowed on the white homespun upon which the patches were set. It scattered the warmth of Dutch bricks, of Dutch hearths, Dutch cheeks. Rebecca saw that the Leffertses' quilt had more patches than the one being quilted at Mrs. Scott's bee.

The girls and women noticed this too. The women hurried through their quilting so that the frames could be rolled up and they could make paper patterns of the star-and-crescent quilt. That was a very great honor. One of the mothers at Mrs. Scott's quilting bee wrote to her old home in Connecticut about it:

February 7, 1841.

We have had deep snow. No teams passed for over three weeks, but as soon as the drifts could be broken, Mary Scott sent her boy Frank around to say that she was going to have a quilting bee. Everybody turned out. She had two big turkeys and her famous currant jelly. One of Mary's new quilts is called the Star-and-Crescent. She got it from Mrs. Lefferts, one of the new Pennsylvania Dutch families. A lot of Dutch are taking up land here in the Reserve.

Rebecca and the other girls, with Frank's help, made butternut taffy in a big kettle hung over the fire in the dining room, candles were lighted, and the quilting party sat down to the turkeys, wheat and rye pancakes with wild honey, succotash, and the pies. It had been a friendly party, the coming together of neighbors to help Frank's mother finish a quilt. She would do the same for them some time.

For young Rebecca the quilting bee was a dream come true. Frank had been kind to her, and the other girls seemed to like her very much. She would join them in school next term, with a copy book, slate and pencil, speller and arithmetic. Together, when school was over, they would play house in the hollow of a giant sycamore tree whose fantastic arched opening made a door. They would shower themselves with blossoms in the Ohio orchards in the spring and, when the fruit was ripe, feast on Buckeye strawberries, Seek-No-Further apples, and Honest-John peaches. All this happiness the star-and-crescent quilt had helped to bring.

"I will be over your way soon!" Frank said, as he showed Rebecca and her mother down the road with a big lantern. Through the door of the Scott homestead came pleasant good-bys from Anntje, Emma, Sophia, and Ellen.

"Thank you for the star-and-crescent pattern. . . ."

"Come and see me, Rebecca Lefferts, and I will exchange patchwork pieces with you. . . ."

"Will you sit beside me in school? . . ."

"We will go for wild flowers when the snow melts. . . ."

So Mrs. Scott and Rebecca's new friends started them happily home.

With them went the star-and-crescent quilt, which was to

gather renown with the years. It became a gift to Rebecca's children and a heritage for their children. It went home to Pennsylvania and lay in fading red-and-white folds in a museum of arts and crafts, for the quilts of our ancestors held American history in their thousands of hand-set stitches. The men and boys blazed trails, but the women and girls stitched stories into their patches of calico, chintz, and homespun.

SYLVANUS'S NEW BREECHES

As soon as Sylvanus Whitcher came down the ladder from
his attic bedroom, he knew what was going to happen that
day. He understood why he had been relieved by his brother
Samuel from digging stumps in the new corn field. Drawn
up close to the sunny kitchen window was the family rocking chair with its bright turkey-red cushion. The ironing
board was placed on one end of the table. On the back of
the stove stood the tailor's goose, a flatiron used for doing
heavy pressing, with a sharply pointed end and a red handle
shaped like the neck of a goose. Carefully hung over the back
of the rocking chair was a length of new strong pepper-and-
salt homespun suiting. Miss Martha Norris, the tailoress of

their little back-town, Coventry-Benton in the White Mountains, must be expected; she was surely coming to measure and fit Sylvanus's new clothes. Once a year Miss Martha made the rounds of all the homes where there were boys and made them new homespun breeches and jackets, sewed with such small honest stitches that the clothes lasted until the next year and often longer. There was nothing wrong with Miss Martha's sewing. The trouble was with the boys.

Sylvanus had grown three inches the past year. With only ten weeks of school in the winter and eight or ten in the summer, with so much work in the fields and with Sugar Loaf, Owl's Head, and Blueberry Mountains to roam over, a boy of that time, 1850, was bound to grow fast. His legs had stretched amazingly. The sleeves of his old jacket hardly covered his wrists. Certainly Sylvanus needed new breeches, for the ones he put on so hurriedly that morning were patched. This was the boy's trouble. Now that he was thirteen and tall for his age, he wanted a suit with long trousers, a well-fitting suit. Miss Martha had only one paper pattern for a boy's breeches and she tried to make it fit every boy, little or big, in Coventry-Benton. From so much changing and altering, this breeches pattern had lost its original shape. Miss Martha's tailoring was in demand by all the mothers in town, but the stout clothes she turned out had neither form nor style. Sylvanus had seen a boy from Wells River at the last singing school at the meeting house, wearing long, store-bought trousers. He had looked very fine indeed and he was popular with the girls. Especially was Dorcas Stevens, Sylvanus's girl neighbor, interested in the boy in the store clothes. It did not seem to Sylvanus that he could live through another year in a pair of Miss Martha's home-made breeches.

Sylvanus grudgingly ate his breakfast of mush and milk, crisply browned salt pork, and flapjacks. He made a wide circle of the kitchen so as to avoid that piece of homespun that seemed to be woven into the very heart of the boy. Sylvanus knew even the old sheep from which the wool had come, having followed it several years to and from the hill pasture. He had helped with the shearing, washing, carding, and rolling of the wool from which his mother and sisters had spun and woven the cloth. It was the same color, mixed black and white, as all his other breeches. The store clothes that were beginning to be shown in the larger New England towns were smartly dyed blue or brown. Suddenly Sylvanus made a decision. He got his cap and muffler from the peg on the wall behind the door, put them on, and slipped out before his mother had a chance to ask his help with the day's chores. He did not know exactly where he was going, but it was somewhere to avoid Miss Martha with her tailor's thimble, snipping shears, and mouthful of pins. As a matter of fact, Sylvanus was running away.

Coventry-Benton was folded in a hollow below the White Mountains of New Hampshire. The season was neither winter nor spring, but that in-between time when the green of mosses and lichen could be seen where the snow was light or had melted, and a circle of cedars and hemlocks wreathed the little town. Snowbirds were still about, flirting their saucy white tail feathers, but the mountain whistlers, piping their tunes about awakened brooks, could also be heard.

It was hard going for the ox sledges along rutted roads, but ice on Whitcher Brook and Tunnel Stream was cracking. There was a warmth in the sunshine. "Good sugar weather!" Sylvanus said to himself, and that gave him an idea. He would run away to some purpose; he would try to go as far as Mr. Benton-French's sugar grove and see if extra help was needed. It was near the time of year when boys were in great demand in the maple-sugar camp that provided the town with its main industry. Mr. French owned one thousand tall, straight sugar-maple trees five miles from Coventry-Benton, across Coventry Meadows and up the side of the mountain. Sylvanus had worked for him the season before.

The snow that was left, the song of the mountain whistler, the cold wind blowing inside his muffler made Sylvanus remember the fun of sugaring off. It was always so still and white in the sugar camp, the only sound that of the drop, drip, drop of the sweet sap from the spouts thrust into notches in the tree trunks; drip, drip, dripping into the dug-out butternut-wood trough set in the snow beneath each spout. The snow had to be cleared away for the big fire. Then the boys, with pails hung on yokes from their shoulders, gathered the maple sap from the troughs and poured it into big iron kettles to be boiled over the fire. In the evening, if they stayed all night in the sugar camp, perhaps a sleighload of girls would come up the mountain to eat a picnic supper, stuff themselves with maple sugar, sing, tell stories, and then ride off home to the tune of the jingling sleigh bells. Yes, Sylvanus would be miles away by the time the town tailoress arrive

He found it easy going through the Hollow, where the main buildings of the town lay. The farms were scattered, but here, like huddled toy buildings, were the white meeting house, the post office kept by Uncle Amos and Aunt Polly Whitcher, the schoolhouse with its rows of plank benches and desks made by the town carpenter, the smithy, the grist mill and the sawmill, and the wheelwright's shop. Coventry-Benton had no store. Everything that Sylvanus's family and the other townsfolk needed was grown or made. The soil was rocky, full of stumps, but rich when once it was cultivated, and the Coventry Meadows afforded rich herd grass for cattle. Because the town raised its own food and had plain tastes, life was simple and pleasant. Sugaring off in the early spring. Making potash in the summer from the wood ashes left from clearing land of old trees and stumps. Pleasant evenings when one went to singing school or had an evening known as a paring bee, when all the neighbors collected in someone's barn to pare apples before drying them for winter use. These everyday activities were all the children knew. Sunday school and the service at early candlelighting in the little white meeting house filled the seventh day of the week.

Sylvanus loved to smell the spruce wood and gather blocks and chips at the shop where the town carpenter made shingles, butter firkins, and clapboards. He liked to join the other boys and girls who crowded the town post office, his Aunt Polly's kitchen, each Wednesday and Saturday, when the post-rider came over the mountain with his saddlebags full of mail. Uncle Amos, the Coventry postmaster, and Aunt Polly emptied the letters and papers on the kitchen table. Then everyone grabbed his own.

Sylvanus reviewed the daily life of his town, which was very satisfying to a boy, as he trudged on until the town boundary was past and he was well up the mountain road that led toward the sugar bush. The snow was deeper here, and the tall trees, whose protection was assured in the town's charter, began to close him in. These woods were the home of bears, wolves, and lynxes. The wolves especially were to be feared, for they often made marauding trips to the farms at night, carrying off a young lamb or a calf. Usually the workers in the sugar bush took a rifle with them.

Sylvanus was not afraid. He was the son of settlers who lived always in the shadow of danger and want, but as the day progressed toward noon and he remembered that he had left home without putting anything to eat in his pocket, he began to hope that he might find the sugar camp in full operation. Some of the boys said that Mr. French had been up there for the last week.

As he climbed the mountain trail, Sylvanus heard the sound of an animal's steps pad-padding along behind him. At first he felt disinclined to look back; he just plodded on. Then a friendly, familiar voice called out: "Hey, there, Sylvanus Whitcher, want a lift?" Sylvanus knew the voice and gratefully climbed into the sledge that drew up beside him, driven by "Pesky Pete" Howe, the town ne'er-do-well, but a great favorite with the children. Pesky Pete never worked unless he was hungry. He owned a lean little mountain horse, and he spent his days driving from one farm, from one village, to the next, trading leaky pots and rusty kettles, cast-off farm tools, lengths of cloth, a bag of grain that had mice in it, anything that he could barter for something else as useless. The sound of a cat's mewing came from the back of the sledge.

"Got a pussy back there in a bag," Pete explained to Sylvanus. "Picked her up ten miles back in the country and figure to take her about twenty miles further on. I heard of a mill at Wells River that needs a good mousing pussy and will pay twenty-five cents for her."

They jogged on but had not gone very far when, with a last yowl of protest, the cat escaped, leaping like a rabbit through the woods. Pete stopped and ran after her. "Here, pussy, good pussy," he called, until his voice was only an echo coming back to Sylvanus by way of the trees. The horse stood patiently cropping the moss beneath the snow, and Sylvanus started on again by foot. Pete might spend the rest of the day trying to recapture his cat. There was no use waiting for him.

It was early in the afternoon when fresh ruts in the road leading to the sugar bush showed Sylvanus that someone had driven up within the last few days. Rows of tall sugar maples met him, and he wandered in and out among them looking for traces of the sugar workers. No one was there. The camp seemed to be empty until at last the smell of a smoky wood fire and the sound of a hammer led the boy to a spot in the center of the bush where he saw a man busily hammering basswood spouts into the notched tree trunks. There were no troughs placed as yet beneath the spouts. It was too early for the sap to rise.

It was Mr. French himself, the owner of the maple-sugar grove. He was cutting notches about five feet from the ground in the new growth of trees in which the sap would be tapped for the first time. He had a large supply of new spouts, which he and his men had whittled during the long winter. He looked up as he saw the boy.

"Why, hello there, Sylvanus," he called. "You took a long walk today! No, I am not hiring any boys for a week or two yet. The troughs are not ready, and there is no use starting sugaring off until we are sure of a good steady flow of sap. Watch for a notice in the post office, 'Boy Wanted,' soon. I shall be waiting for you, Sylvanus."

Sylvanus started slowly down the mountain trail. Of course Mr. French supposed that he had brought his lunch along or he would have offered to share with the boy that frying pan of bacon sizzling over a beechwood fire and perfuming the cold air. Sylvanus's feet were tired, and he began to realize that he truly needed new clothes. His jacket and breeches were worn thin.

He trudged along until he came to the spot where he had left Pesky Pete. The horse and sledge were gone. Either the horse had wandered home by itself or Pete had decided that trading a cat was not worth the trouble. It seemed more than twice as far coming down to Coventry-Benton as it had going away. When the afternoon shadows lay across the road and then changed to darkness, Sylvanus thought that he would have to give up. He was hungry, half-frozen, and very sorry that he had left home. He thought of the candle-lighted supper table, of its great piles of golden corn-bread squares, mugs of creamy milk, baked potatoes bursting their jackets, dishes of home-made peach and plum preserves. He picked some checkerberry leaves from beneath the snow and chewed them to appease his appetite. He felt faint, and it

seemed like a dream when a horse and rider loomed out of
the dark forest, with loaded saddlebags, and a lantern hanging on the saddle.

"Have a ride, son?" It was the friendly voice of the post-
rider, bringing the mail bags over the mountain. Sylvanus
gratefully climbed up behind the man, and they started
down through the darkness, the lantern spreading a slender
yellow path, the only sound the occasional hoot of a startled
owl. At last the twinkling of many candles, like stars, below
the lonely riders showed them they had reached the town.
They clattered along the main street and drew up before the
door of the house where Uncle Amos and Aunt Polly Whitcher kept the post office.

The brightly lighted kitchen held a crowd of boys and
girls all anxiously waiting for Uncle Amos to empty the mail
bags onto the wide kitchen table, eager to scramble into the
fascinating mass, read the postmarks and addresses, and fish

out their own letters. Sylvanus was almost too tired to join the cheerful noisy group. As usual, Aunt Polly was scolding because the children pushed so. Uncle Amos usually gave up trying to do the sorting himself. The coming of the mail was a great event. Everybody read all the addresses and post-marks he could and grabbed for his own mail.

"Here are your letters, Sylvanus," Dorcas Stevens said. "Your mother has one from Miss Martha with the Wells River postmark. I know her handwriting." Then she pulled the boy's sleeve. She was all rosy smiles and sparkling eyes, framed by a crimson pumpkin-shaped hood. Her quilted cape had a border of fur. "Will you take me to singing school tomorrow evening, Sylvanus?" Dorcas asked. "I like better to go with you than any other of the boys."

Suddenly Sylvanus's heart felt so light that he forgot all about his discouraging day. Dorcas did not mind his old clothes. He could endure Miss Martha's tailoring for another year, if only she cut the breeches large enough. But why was she writing to his mother on a day when she was expected to be sewing for them?

The mystery was solved as soon as Sylvanus reached home. In the excitement there because the town tailoress had not appeared, no one had missed Sylvanus. He slipped into his place at the supper table and listened as his mother read Miss Martha's letter:

"I am so sorry to miss my days at your house but you will see me next week. I expect to bring back a new pattern for boys' clothes when I return to Coventry-Benton, the jacket longer, with fullness in the breeches."

Sylvanus spread a piece of corn bread thickly with apple

butter and took a bite. The world seemed good to him once more. Dorcas, after all, did not judge him by appearances, and the new suit might fit better than the old one.

Miss Martha, the town tailoress, was left behind in the old handcraft days, and only through the men who grew up in New England and remembered her paper pattern does her story come to us today. Sylvanus's great-grandsons wear custom-made clothes: suits for school, for parties, for tennis, for golf, for riding, for winter, summer, autumn, spring. Wool from Scotland, loomed in England, tailored by a dozen men in a great American city, the finished clothing packed and sent by train thousands of miles to department stores in smaller cities—thus a boy's new suit is provided today. But Sylvanus Whitcher wore his homespun with pride, and his friend, Dorcas Stevens, admired his new suit as much as any boy could desire.

THE FOURTH OF JULY SURPRISE

THE LAST lemon was squeezed, and the pail of sweetened juice was put out in the cool springhouse to be ready in the morning for the Fourth of July lemonade. Louis sat down on the back porch, where there was a cool breeze coming down from the hills. His mother sat down too, with her basket of mending. There was an hour before supper.

Louis, thirteen years old, and his mother had been getting ready for the Fourth of July celebration in their town, Chester, Vermont. On all the green lawns there would be boards laid upon sawhorses, and white tablecloths spread over the boards to hold the food that the Chester housewives were getting ready for the holiday-makers. It made the boy

hungry to think of the good things being prepared in all
the Chester kitchens. Great tin pails of cold lemonade. Sliced
ham as pink as roses. Juicy cucumber pickles. Sandwiches
of every kind. Fluffy rolls and biscuits. Three-decker chocolate cakes. Cold apple and cherry pies. Louis had heard that
there would be a roasted pig on the minister's lawn with
an orange in its mouth. In the morning the entire countryside, in buggies, surreys, hayricks, even farm wagons filled
with wooden chairs for seats, would come to Chester to see
the Fourth of July parade, hear the speeches, and have a free
lunch. Louis could hardly wait for the Fourth but, sitting
there with his mother, he thought that there would be time
for a story before supper.

He wanted to hear the story of his grandfather, Simeon
Ide, that always began the same way:

"Once upon a time, in the winter of 1799, your grandfather was a little boy five years old, and he went on a two-
day journey in an open sleigh with his Uncle Zenas Stone,
to live in Shrewsbury, Massachusetts."

Louis moved closer to his mother and went on with the
story himself. "He had to try to earn his living, a little boy
five years old, because his mother was too poor to take care
of him and his brothers and sisters. . . ."

Then Louis's mother took up the story. "They rode over
mountain trails, through forests where there were bears,
along lonely country roads, with Simeon's feet and hands
almost frozen. Think of it, Louis! But your grandfather
remembers that he sang on the way to keep his courage up.
And this little boy, Simeon Ide, came at last to the farm
where he was to live with relatives and earn his living. That

winter he cut wood for the fireplace and shoveled paths through the snow to the barn to feed the cows. When spring came, he rode a great horse to plow, almost falling off it, because his legs stuck out straight on either side. He carried bags of grist on horseback to be ground at the mill. And he drove his two grandmothers five miles to shop for knitting needles, flowers for their bonnets, and calico.

"He never played and he went to the country school only when there was no farm work a boy of his age could do. He remembers the Shrewsbury parson, a tall stern man in knee breeches, silver shoe buckles, a colored vest, and a ruffled shirt, walking down the Shrewsbury street. Your grandfather, little Simeon Ide, always bowed very low to the parson when he met him. The parson patted his head and told Simeon that he was a good little boy. All through the years Simeon remembered the feeling of the parson's hand on his head, for he was a lonely little boy.

"But Simeon grew to be a year or two older, and his mother sent for him to come home to her farm in Vermont. Simeon had ever so many brothers and sisters, and he went on working with his hands to help them just as he had worked in Shrewsbury. Their house had one fireplace to heat all the rooms. Simeon tugged in the great back-log for the fire, piled on the kindlings and the fore-sticks, hung the dinner pot on the crane, and laid the bare pine table for the children's meals. He worked as hard at home as he had in Shrewsbury; he cut wood, carried water, tended the sheep, plowed, and harvested. When Simeon was fifteen years old, he was bound out to a printer to learn the trade. Though he knew how to use his hands so well, he had also read so much geography and history that he did not need to go to school any longer.

"A printer's shop in those long-ago days was a place of handwork. There was a hand-lever press and a printing machine that was worked with the printer's foot. Two or three cases held the type, small bits of lead with a letter raised on one end. This type was not arranged in alphabetical order, but those letters that were most often used were nearest to hand. Simeon had to take out the type as fast as his hands could move, spell the words to be printed by slipping the letters in an odd-shaped box called a composing stick, and ink the type with balls of sheep's wool. Then the composing stick was put into the press under the sheets of paper to be printed. Simeon's master owned the *Vermont Republican,* a little newspaper that, in addition to news, printed advertisements of sword knots and epaulets, maple syrup, woodenware, and sometimes warned the villagers that a bear had been seen coming down from the mountains toward the sheep pastures."

Louis took up the story, for it always sounded at this point like a wonder tale. "And my grandfather, Simeon Ide, while he was still a boy, went out to seek his fortune and met the great Mr. Noah Webster, who let him print his new spelling book and his dictionary. Simeon and his little sister, who was only eleven years old, had their own printing shop in a deserted blacksmith shop. Simeon at last bought the *Vermont Republican* and edited it himself. He printed the New Testament by hand. He printed almanacs, stitching the pages together with needle and thread, for there were no binding machines in those days. Once he walked sixty miles over

the Vermont hills, with his clothes tied up in a big silk handkerchief, on his way to get work in a bookshop. He bought the type and printing press for his shop with his savings."

"He is a great man here in Vermont," Louis's mother said. "How he would enjoy our Fourth of July celebration, but your grandfather is eighty-four years old now, Louis."

"Yes, of course, Grandfather is too old to celebrate now," Louis said.

Beyond the town they could see the Green Mountains. An old road took its way from Chester out toward the hills. It had been a deer and Indian trail first, then a cow path, and later had been widened by farm wagons. Now the country people were thronging in over these roads to keep Fourth of July in Chester.

Louis and his mother could see a man coming down the hill road on foot. He carried a cane and his clothes were dusty, but he came as straight and swiftly as an Indian. Teams stopped to offer him a lift, but he thanked the drivers and walked on. Nearer and nearer he came. At last he turned into the Chester street. Louis shouted: "Mother, there's Grandfather!" They ran to meet him.

"Thought I'd come and help you celebrate Independence Day," said the old man. Simeon Ide, eighty-four years old, pioneer printer of Vermont, had walked twenty-seven miles in the hot July sun to keep the holiday with Louis and his mother.

He said that he was not even tired. Before going to bed he retold the story of his little-boy days to Louis. They both got up at five o'clock in the morning and went down to the

Chester Common to see the carpenters put up the platform where the band would play and the speakers stand to make their speeches.

"Who do you think will make the big speech, Grandfather?" Louis asked.

"Well, I wouldn't like to say for certain about that," said Simeon Ide. "They always ask a big man, a patriot, to make the oration."

After breakfast there was the parade. Louis thought there could never be any town affair so interesting. The parade was almost a mile long, from the Horribles, with masks, stuffed suits, and drums made of barrels, to the schoolchildren dressed in white and carrying flags. The town fire-engine was in the parade, the old soldiers marched, and there was a brass band, the cymbals and horns sparkling in the July sun. All the trades that had helped make the town a good place in which to live were shown: the farmer breaking and beating his flax; the blacksmith with his sledge-hammer, vise, and anvil; the printer with his press on a float from which he tossed off ink-wet copies of the Declaration of Independence. Whoever was hungry or thirsty stopped at some friendly picnic table along the line of march for a sandwich and a glass of lemonade.

Louis followed the parade, keeping step with the band and waving a flag. He went with the other children toward the Common, where the speaking was to take place. Once he looked back to see if his grandfather was coming along, but he was not.

He thought: "Grandfather is such an old man that he needs to rest after walking twenty-seven miles yesterday.

Mother must have asked him to take a nap so he could enjoy the fireworks after supper."

He reached the Common and sat down on a bench near the platform, which smelled of fresh wood and was draped with red, white, and blue bunting. The minister, the town officers, and the school principal sat on it, high above Louis's head, but where was the speaker? It was a great honor to make the Fourth of July oration, Louis knew. The towns-people remembered and thought about what the speaker said until the next Fourth of July came. At the back of the platform there was a flight of steps. Suddenly the band struck up "Hail to the Chief." The people on the platform stood, and up the steps, out to the front, came Grandfather Simeon Ide!

Louis was too surprised to join in the hand-clapping and cheers that greeted the Fourth of July speaker. He thought of his grandfather as a story, a very old man walking over the mountain to visit his daughter and his grandson, a little boy of long-ago taking big bags of grist to a mill, or sitting on a high stool to set type for Mr. Webster's speller. But there he was, the great man of the day, standing on the platform. In a loud, clear voice, Grandfather Simeon Ide began to speak.

"What day is this?" he asked.

"Fourth of July, grandfather," Louis shouted up to him.

"Well, yes," Simeon Ide said, "but I like to call it Independence Day, the day when a boy of the colonies called Sam began to grow up and learned that he and all the American people could be independent through the work of their hands."

How the people cheered that! They liked everything that Simeon Ide went on to say about the work, the hand skill, the courage that had made their town and all the towns of New England independent. When his grandfather's speech was over, Louis could hardly reach him because so many people crowded around to shake Simeon Ide's hand. There had not been such a great Independence Day speech in Chester for a long time.

Louis and his grandfather walked home hand in hand. "Could you teach me to set type?" Louis asked.

"Why, yes, I could do that," Simeon Ide said. "I could stay a week or so here in Chester and we could set up a press out in the woodshed. I could get some old type down at the newspaper office, and then you and the other boys could print your own newspaper. But machinery is going to do all our printing soon. Pioneer printers like me are going out of fashion."

After supper Louis and his grandfather sent off torpedoes and sky-rockets and lighted red fire in the front yard. It had been their best Independence Day. The next day they began setting up Louis's printing shop in the woodshed. It was fun, but Louis found it hard to pick up the type and arrange the letters as fast as his grandfather could. As Louis walked part way toward the mountain road with him, and told him good-by at the end of the town, the boy felt as if his best story had come true. This man, Simeon Ide, was great; he had been a brave boy, and he was Louis's own grandfather.

Louis grew up and wrote the story of Simeon Ide. It was printed by machines, for the days of hand-presses are gone. The dictionaries and Bibles that the boy Simeon of long-ago printed by hand are now made by machines. But the early printers of our country, setting their type, propelling their presses by hand and foot, gave us the first records from which grew our books and newspapers of today.

BOOK TRAILS

CHILD LIFE IN COLONIAL DAYS, by Alice Morse Earle. The Macmillan Co., New York.

HOME LIFE IN COLONIAL DAYS, by Alice Morse Earle. Grosset & Dunlap, New York.

HOMESPUN HANDICRAFTS, by Ella Shannon Bowles. J. B. Lippincott Co., Philadelphia, Pa.

EARLY AMERICAN CRAFTSMEN, by Walter A. Dyer. Appleton-Century Co., New York.

CUSTOMS AND FASHIONS IN OLD NEW ENGLAND, by Alice Morse Earle. Charles Scribner's Sons, New York.

THE ARTS AND CRAFTS OF NEW ENGLAND, by George Francis Dow. The Wayside Press, Topsfield, Mass.

ABOUT ANTIQUES, by Ella Shannon Bowles. J. B. Lippincott Co., Philadelphia, Pa.

THE SAMPLER

AMERICAN SAMPLERS, by Ethel Stanwood Bolton and Eva Johnson Coe. Society of Colonial Dames of America, Library of Congress, Washington, D. C.

THE PLEASURES OF COLLECTING (Chapter VIII on samplers), by Gardner Teall. Appleton-Century Co., New York.

THE DEVELOPMENT OF EMBROIDERY IN AMERICA, by Candace Wheeler. Harper & Brothers, New York.

THE CLOCK-MAKER'S APPRENTICE

THE CLOCK BOOK, by Wallace Nutting. Old America Co., Framingham, Mass.

CHATS ON HOUSEHOLD CURIOS, by Fred W. Burgess. Frederick A. Stokes Co., New York.

CONNECTICUT CLOCKMAKERS OF THE EIGHTEENTH CENTURY, by Penrose Hookes. Dodd, Mead & Co., New York.

FURNITURE OF THE PILGRIM CENTURY, by Wallace Nutting. Marshall Jones Co., Boston, Mass.

THE SILVERSMITH'S ADVENTURE

MAKERS OF EARLY AMERICAN SILVER, by Robert Ensko. R. Ensko, New York.

EARLY AMERICAN SILVER, by C. Louise Avery. Appleton-Century Co., New York.

HISTORIC SILVER OF THE COLONIES, by Francis H. Bigelow. The Macmillan Co., New York.

AMERICAN SILVER, by Richard T. Halsey. Museum of Fine Arts, Boston, Mass.

THE GARDEN MERCY PLANTED

OLD-TIME GARDENS, by Alice Morse Earle. The Macmillan Co., New York.

GARDENS OF COLONY AND STATE, by Alice G. Lockwood. Charles Scribner's Sons, New York.

THE BOY WHO LOVED TOOLS

COLONIAL FURNITURE IN AMERICA, by Luke V. Vincent. Charles Scribner's Sons, New York.

THE PINE FURNITURE OF EARLY NEW ENGLAND, by Russell H. Kittell. Doubleday, Doran & Co., Garden City, New York.

THE HOMES OF OUR ANCESTORS (about the American Wing Collections, Metropolitan Museum of Art, New York City), by Richard T. Halsey. Doubleday, Doran & Co., Garden City, New York.

THE AMERICAN RENAISSANCE, by Theodore M. Dilloway. Brown-Robertson, New York.

COLONIAL HOMES AND THEIR FURNISHINGS, by Mary H. Northend. Little, Brown & Co., Boston, Mass.

FURNITURE OF THE PILGRIM CENTURY by Wallace Nutting. Old America Co., Framingham, Mass.

THE FURNITURE OF OUR FOREFATHERS, by Esther Singleton. Doubleday, Doran & Co., Garden City, New York.

BETSY'S NEW HAT

COSTUME OF COLONIAL DAYS, by Alice Morse Earle. Charles Scribner's Sons, New York.

TWO CENTURIES OF COSTUME IN AMERICA, by Alice Morse Earle. The Macmillan Co., New York.

HISTORIC DRESS IN AMERICA, by Elizabeth McClellan. G. W. Jacobs, Philadelphia, Pa.

EARLY AMERICAN COSTUME, by Edward Warwick and Henry C. Pitz. Appleton-Century Co., New York.

ROMANCE IN OLD PHILADELPHIA, by John T. Faris. J. B. Lippincott Co., Philadelphia, Pa.

COVERED-WAGON BOY

THE COVERED WAGON, by Emerson Hough. Appleton-Century Co., New York.

COVERED-WAGON DAYS, by Albert J. Dickson. Arthur H. Clark Co., Cleveland, Ohio.

THE CONESTOGA WAGON, by Bryan Hamilton. New Jersey Historical Society, Newark, N. J.

LOST IN THE APPLE CAVE

JOHNNY APPLESEED, by James L. Himrod. Chicago Historical Society, Chicago, Illinois.

JOHNNY APPLESEED, by Eleanor Atkinson. Harper & Brothers, New York.

THE ADVENTURES OF JOHNNY APPLESEED, by Henry Chapin. Coward-McCann, New York.

A BASKET FOR THANKSGIVING

INDIAN BASKETRY, by Otis T. Mason. Doubleday, Doran & Co., Garden City, New York.

QUILT OF MANY STARS

A BOOK OF HAND-WOVEN COVERLETS, by Eliza Calvert Hall. Little, Brown & Co., Boston, Mass.

QUILTS: THEIR STORY AND HOW TO MAKE THEM, by Marie D. Webster. Doubleday, Doran & Co., Garden City, New York.

ONE HUNDRED AND ONE PATCHWORK PATTERNS, by Ruby S. McKim. McKim Studios, Independence, Missouri.

HANDCRAFTS IN THE HOME (old-time quilting), by Mabel T. Priestman. A. C. McClurg & Co., Chicago, Illinois.

CHRISTMAS SHIP

OLD SALEM, by Eleanor Putnam. Houghton Mifflin Co., Boston, Mass.

THE OLD SHIPMASTERS OF SALEM, by Charles E. Trow. G. P. Putnam's Sons, New York.

THE BOOK OF OLD SHIPS, by Henry B. Culver. Doubleday, Doran & Co., Garden City, New York.

OLD SHIP FIGURE-HEADS, by L. G. Laughton. Halton and T. Smith, London, England.

HISTORIC FIGURE-HEADS, by Frank H. Severance. Buffalo Historical Society, Buffalo, N. Y.

THE FOURTH OF JULY SURPRISE

THE NEW ENGLAND PRIMER, by Paul L. Ford. Dodd, Mead & Co., New York.

THE COLONIAL PRINTER, by Lawrence C. Wroth. The Grolier Society, New York, and Library of Congress, Washington, D. C.

BENJAMIN FRANKLIN, PRINTER, by John C. Oswald. Doubleday, Doran & Co., Garden City, New York.

Besides these books, more about American handcrafts can be learned from local historical societies and from the back numbers of these magazines: *The Antiquarian* and *Country Life in America.*